Technology: A
Failure

CYRIL · Units 12B–13B

Stress corrosion cracking

Prepared by the Course Team

Compendium of Your Reference and Instructional Literature

The Open University

Failure of Stressed Materials Course Team

Open University Staff

Nick Reid	(Chairman, Reader in Materials Science)
Kris Acharia	(Photographer, HEK)
Richard Black	(Technical Staff)
Keith Cavanagh	(Editor)
David Crabbe	(Lecturer in Materials Science)
Adrian Demaid	(Lecturer in Materials Science)
Joel Greenberg	(Academic Computing Service)
Andy Harding	(Course Manager)
Reinhold Hermann	(Project Officer)
Geoff Holister	(Professor of Engineering Science)
Roy Lawrance	(Graphic Artist)
Rob Lyon	(Designer)
Jim Moffatt	(Technical Staff)
Ian Norman	(Technical Staff)
Ken Reynolds	(Staff Tutor)
Graham Weaver	(Senior Lecturer in Materials Science)
Keith Williams	(Lecturer in Materials Science)

Consultants

Charles Booker	(City of London Polytechnic)
Roger Davidge	(Atomic Energy Research Establishment, Harwell)
Ian Howard	(University of Sheffield)
Alan Lawley	(Drexel University, Philadelphia, USA)
Charles May	(City of London Polytechnic)
Nigel Mills	(University of Birmingham)
Alan Rosenfield	(Battelle Memorial Institute, Columbus, Ohio, USA)
Rod Smith	(Engineering Laboratory, University of Cambridge)
David Tabor	(Cavendish Laboratory, University of Cambridge)
Pip Youngman	

BBC

Hendrik Ball
Tony Jolly
David Nelson
Martin Wright

The Open University, Walton Hall, Milton Keynes.

First published 1983. Reprinted 1989, 1995.

Copyright © 1985 The Open University.

Filmset by Speedlith Photo Litho Ltd., Manchester.

Printed in the United Kingdom by Halstan & Co. Ltd., Amersham, Bucks.

ISBN 0 335 17154 0

This text forms part of the correspondence element of an Open University Third Level Course.

For general availability of supporting material referred to in this text, please write to Open University Educational Enterprises Limited, 12 Cofferidge Close, Stony Stratford, Milton Keynes, MK11 1BY, Great Britain.

Further information on Open University courses may be obtained from The Admissions Office, The Open University, P.O. Box 48, Milton Keynes MK7 6AB.

1.3

Contents

Unit 12B

1 Brasses

1.1 Copper alloys

Brasses are a family of copper alloys. In general, copper has three main virtues which account for its popularity:

nobility: an inherent resistance to chemical attack by natural atmospheres, apart from some tarnishing;

conductivity: pure copper is an outstanding conductor of heat and electricity (exceeded only by silver);

ductility: the ability to be stretched extensively before breaking; this property allows the metal to be severely deformed during shaping operations.

Unfortunately, pure copper has quite low strength and the purpose of most alloying additions is to strengthen it, while retaining the nobility. Such additions invariably reduce the conductivity, but a range of dilute copper alloys has been developed which strike a compromise between conductivity and high strength. These *high conductivity alloys* contain small ($<4\%$) additions of *cadmium*, *beryllium*, *chromium* or *iron* to give enhanced strength without drastic reductions in conductivity.

A summary of the compositions, properties and applications of the most important copper-base alloys is given in Table 1; we are interested in the brasses in this case study.

Brasses are mixtures of copper and zinc; they are the most important group of copper alloys owing to their wide range of mechanical properties. They are resistant to atmospheric and marine corrosion, pleasing in colour and relatively inexpensive. The extra cost of alloying is somewhat offset by the lower cost of zinc (£450 tonne^{-1}) compared to that of copper (£1100 tonne^{-1})*.

* Prices in February 1983.

1.2 Phases and microstructures of brasses

The existence of phases in an alloy system under equilibrium conditions is usually described with the aid of a *phase or equilibrium diagram*. The copper-rich end of the phase diagram for the copper–zinc system of alloys is shown in Figure 1 (the other end is of little interest to engineers).

> When solid, pure copper is crystalline (of course), with a face-centred cubic (fcc) crystal structure. What is the structure of the α-phase in Figure 1?
>
> ---
>
> Since the α-phase region of Figure 1 extends to include the composition of pure copper at all temperatures up to the melting point, it follows that the structure of the α-phase must be the same as that of copper — fcc.

The α-phase is an fcc solid solution, that is it consists of an almost random ('disordered') mixture of copper and zinc atoms located on fcc lattice points (Figure 2a). Similarly, the β-phase is a disordered solid solution having the body-centred cubic (bcc) crystal structure (Figure 2b). The phase β′ is simply a form of β-phase in which there is *long-range order* of the copper and zinc atoms (as opposed to a random mixture), see Figure 2c.

When there is perfect order, it requires equal numbers of copper and zinc atoms (there is one Cu and one Zn atom per unit cell in Figure 2c) and that is why the β′-phase is found only in alloys around 50 Cu/50 Zn.

Table 1 Some important copper-base alloys

	B.S. specifications	Composition (%) (Balance Cu)	Condition	Typical mechanical properties				Characteristics and uses
				0·1% P.S. N/mm^2	Tensile strength N/mm^2	Elongation (%)	Hardness (VPN)	
Brasses	2870	30 Zn	Annealed Hard	77 510	325 695	70 5	65 185	Cartridge brass: deep-drawing brass, having maximum ductility of the copper–zinc alloys
	2870	37 Zn	Annealed Hard	95 540	340 725	55 4	65 185	'Common brass': a general purpose alloy suitable for limited forming operations by cold-work
	2870	40 Zn	Hot-rolled	110	370	40	75	Hot-rolled plate used for tube plates of condensers. Also as extruded rods and tubes. Limited capacity for cold-work
	2870	Mn Al up to Fe 7% total Sn 37 Zn	Grade A Grade B	230 280	465 540	20 15	— —	High-tensile brass: wrought sections for pump rods, etc. Cast alloys: marine propellors, water turbine runners, rudders. Locomotive axle boxes
Tin bronzes	2870	3·75 Sn 0·10 P	Annealed Hard	110 620	340 740	65 5	60 210	Low-tin bronze: good elastic properties combined with corrosion resistance. Springs and instrument parts
	1400	10 Sn 0·5 P	Sand-cast	125	280	15	90	Cast phosphor bronze: mainly bearings—cast as sticks for machining of small bearing bushes
	1400	10 Sn 2 Zn	Sand-cast	125	295	16	85	'Admiralty gunmetal': pumps, valves and miscellaneous castings, particularly for marine purposes because of good corrosion resistance. Also statuary because of good casting properties
Aluminium bronzes	2870	5 Al Ni up to Mn 4·0% total	Annealed Hard	125 590	385 775	70 4	80 220	Imitation jewellery, etc. Excellent resistance to corrosion and to oxidation on heating, hence used in engineering particularly in tube form
	1400	9·5 Al 2·5 Fe Ni up to Mn 1·0% each	Cast	185	525	30	115	The best-known aluminium bronze for both sand- and die-casting. Corrosion-resistant castings
Cupro-nickels	2870	25 Ni 0·25 Mn	Annealed Hard		355 600	45 5	80 170	Mainly for coinage, e.g. the current British 'silver' coinage
	3073	68 Ni 1·25 Fe 1·25 Mn	Annealed Hard	215 570	540 725	45 20	120 220	Monel Metal: Combines good mechanical properties with excellent corrosion resistance. Mainly in chemical engineering plant

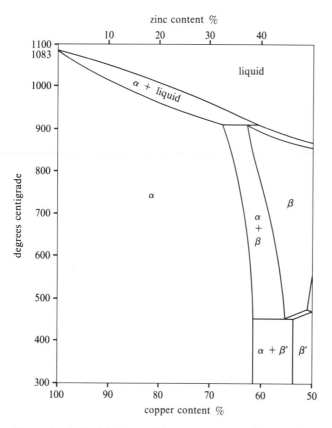

Figure 1   A simplified part of the copper–zinc equilibrium phase diagram

Which phase(s) is present in a brass containing 70% by weight of copper, when brought to equilibrium at 600 °C?

This composition (70% copper) and temperature (600 °C) are the coordinates of a point in Figure 1. This point lies within the area labelled 'α', so the alloy will consist entirely of α-phase, at this temperature.

All brasses with copper contents below about 70% are of this type and are known as **alpha brasses**. Their microstructures are relatively simple in the annealed state, consisting of grains of α-phase (see Figure 3). Additions of zinc in alpha brasses increase both the strength and the elongation-to-fracture, as you can see from Figure 4a; at any given composition, the strength *increases* as the grain size decreases (Figure 4b). Alpha brasses are even more ductile than copper at ambient temperatures, and therefore they are particularly well suited to cold-working into the form of sheet, strip, wire and tube. This enhancement of ductility occurs

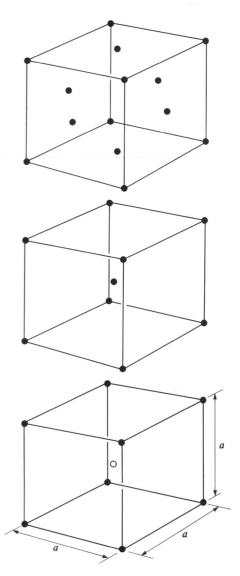

Figure 2   Crystal structures of phases in brass (a) α phase (b) β phase (c) β′ phase

*Figure 3   Annealed grains of alpha brass; notice that some of the grains have perfectly straight segments of boundary; these are special cases of a grain boundary called **annealing twins** (the grains on either side of the boundary are mirror images of one another) and they are a characteristic feature of annealed copper alloys*

because additions of zinc increase the work-hardening rate ($d\sigma/d\varepsilon$) of alpha brass, which in turn postpones the onset of necking (and fracture) until larger strains (Section 1.4.2, Unit 1B). The most ductile of the alpha brasses is '70/30' (Cu/Zn) or 'cartridge' brass, so-called because it is used to make ammunition cartridges. As you will see, the cartridge shaping process which is used demands high ductility.

As you can see from Figure 4c, the elongation-to-fracture increases with the grain size, reaching a maximum when the grain diameter is about 1/10 the thickness.

> Which phases are present in brass containing 60% by weight of copper brought to equilibrium at 500 °C? What are the relative proportions of these phases?

This composition (60% copper) and temperature (500 °C) defines a point in Figure 1. This point lies within the region labelled '$\alpha + \beta$', so the alloy consists of a mixture of α-phase grains and β-phase grains. The relative proportions are given by the *lever rule*:

$$\frac{\text{weight of } \alpha \text{ phase}}{\text{weight of } \beta \text{ phase}} = \frac{bc}{ab} \simeq 3 \text{ (Figure 5)}$$

Copper–zinc alloys of this type are known as **alpha–beta brasses**. They have a 'duplex' microstructure that consists of α grains and β grains (Figure 6). There is a slight difference of colour between the two phases which can be further distinguished by etching—any annealing twins are in the α-phase. Actually, at room temperature the 'β' phase will be β', the ordered phase. This phase is rather hard and brittle with the result that the elongation-to-fracture at room temperature falls dramatically in alpha–beta brasses, and the strength rises sharply, as you can see in Figure 4a. However, if these alloys are heated to above 500 °C, where the beta phase has the disordered form, high ductility returns. Accordingly, alpha–beta brasses are hot-worked (or cast) to shape rather than cold-worked. Hot-working is usually carried out by rolling, extrusion or stamping at temperatures in the range 600–800 °C. Because of the loss of ductility at high zinc contents, brasses are not normally made with less than about 55% copper.

1.3 Heat treatment

The effect of cold-working metals is to cause work-hardening and a decrease in ductility (examples in Table 1). When examined under the microscope, the grains of a cold-worked metal are very distorted and

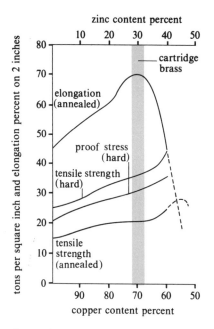

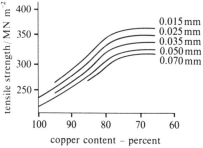

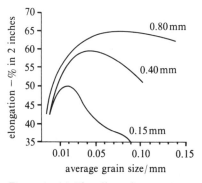

Figure 4 (a) The effect of composition on the mechanical properties of rolled alpha brass sheet. (b) The effect of composition and grain size on the tensile strength of alpha brass. (c) The effect of grain size on the elongation-to-fracture for three thicknesses of testpiece

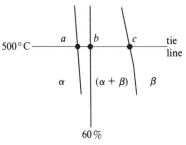

Figure 5 Application of the lever rule to find the relative quantities of phases in a phase mixture

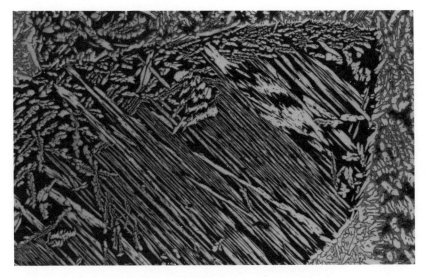

Figure 6 A phase mixture of α grains (the lighter areas) and β grains

elongated in the working direction — indeed, they are hard to see (however, the metal is still entirely crystalline). As you know from Section 5.6 of T252, provided the metal is not irrevocably damaged by cold-working (e.g. cracked), these changes can be reversed by *annealing* — heating for a given time at a given temperature. The annealing time is determined mainly by the time required for the workpiece completely to attain the furnace temperature and this may extend to several hours for a large furnace charge. If the temperature is high enough (600 °C or above for brass), a complete reformation of the grain structure occurs—*recrystal lisation*. The average diameter of the reformed grains (for a given heat treatment) varies *inversely* with the amount of cold-work (e.g. reduction in thickness). After recrystallisation, the grain size may increase with time (*grain growth*), an effect which increases with temperature.

Annealing at too high a temperature should be avoided. Apart from the extra expense in fuel and process time, a high annealing temperature has two adverse effects: it increases the recrystallised grain size and this may cause an *orange peel effect* (a visible roughening of the surface which appears during subsequent cold-working of the workpiece); to avoid this, brass should have a grain size no bigger than 0.03–0.04 mm. The second adverse effect also involves the surface: the formation of more tarnishing and scaling due to oxidation by the air. This can be virtually eliminated by the use of an oxygen-free atmosphere (at a price), but this does not prevent the tendency of zinc to vaporise preferentially leaving a copper-coloured surface. This (and any scaling) can be removed by 'pickling' in dilute acid.

Cold-worked brass can also be annealed at temperatures too low to cause recrystallisation. If this causes a change in properties (such as hardness) back towards their original values without a change of grain structure, the effect is called *recovery*.

1.4 Summary

- Brasses are copper–zinc alloys containing up to about 45% by weight of zinc.
- Up to about 35% zinc, the alloys are *alpha-brasses*, single phase alloys composed of a face-centred cubic solid solution.
- Additions of zinc to alpha brasses cause an increases in strength, the rate of work-hardening $\left(\dfrac{d\sigma}{d\varepsilon}\right)$ and the elongation-to-fracture (ductility).
- Containing about 30% zinc, 'cartridge brass' is the most ductile of the brasses and is normally shaped by cold-working.
- *Alpha–beta brasses* contain 35–45% zinc and are composed of a mixture of α grains and grains of the beta phase. This phase has a body-centred cubic crystal structure and its solid solutions are disordered at temperatures above about 450 °C and below they show *long-range order* (β' phase). These brasses are stronger and less ductile than alpha brasses, and they are normally hot-worked to shape.
- Cold-working causes hardening and loss of ductility. These properties may be restored by *annealing*, either by causing *recrystallisation* at temperatures of about 600 °C and above, or by *recovery* at lower temperatures.

SAQ 1 (*Revision of T252*)

With the aid of Figure 1, describe the chain of events that occurs when a sample of 70/30 Cu–Zn is cooled slowly from the liquid state. State any assumptions made.

How might these events be changed if the alloy were cooled quickly?

2 Shaping sheet metals

A very high proportion of brass in everyday use, from a fountain pen shell to a motor car radiator, has been fabricated from sheet by one of the '*press forming*' processes. This includes many specific operations of which cupping, drawing (and deep drawing), spinning and ironing are examples. Since most of the problems of season-cracking have been reported in products made using these operations, it is these processes that we shall consider in more detail.

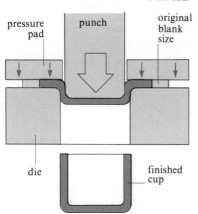

Figure 7 Deep-drawing of a metal disc to form a cup

2.1 Cupping and (deep) drawing

This is a process for producing cup-shaped objects from flat metal discs by punching the metal through a die, as illustrated in Figure 7. I will confine discussion to the drawing of *cylindrical* cups because of its relevance to the case study. Drawing is called 'deep' when the depth of the cup exceeds 50% of its diameter.

Consider the circular blank shown in Figure 8, and try to visualise the change in shape that it will suffer when it is drawn to a cup. The disc can be regarded as having three concentric regions. The central region is in contact with the end of the punch.

> When a force is applied to the punch, what kind of stresses (in sign and direction) do you expect to be set up in the central region?
>
> ───────────────────────────
>
> Membrane stresses — two equal, tensile, principal stresses in the plane of the sheet (rather like the stresses in the ends of a cylindrical thin-walled pressure vessel).

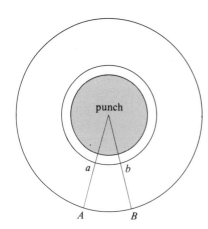

Figure 8 Three concentric regions of a circular blank; during deep-drawing the length AB contracts to ab

The outer region is an annulus which is going to be drawn into the hole within the die. Consider what happens to a length of the circumference, say *AB* in Figure 8.

> What is the sign and direction of the principal stresses that you would expect to exist in the outer region during drawing?
>
> ───────────────────────────
>
> The length *AB* must contract by plastic deformation to *ab* in order to fit into the hole in the die, and this will require a *compressive hoop stress*. To displace *AB* to *ab* will also require a *tensile radial stress*.

The contraction in *AB* must be accompanied by an *increase* in thickness, of course, because plastic deformation causes little if any change in the volume of the metal. The existence of the compressive hoop stress requires the use of the blank-holder in Figure 7. Its function is to hold down the blank on the die, thereby preventing puckering or wrinkling of the disc as it is drawn into the die. As it enters the die, material is first bent over the die radius and then straightened out again as it becomes part of the cup wall.

> Describe the sign and direction of the principal stresses in the cup wall during drawing.
>
> ───────────────────────────
>
> The punch force sets up a *tensile stress* along the (vertical) axis of the cup. In addition, there is a *tensile hoop stress* and a *compressive radial stress* exerted by the sides of the punch.

The latter two stresses can be thought of as arising from the first: when the cup walls are stretched by the axial tensile stress, they shrink against the punch, thereby setting up a hoop tension and a radial compression. These stresses cause some thinning of the wall and this is greatest at the shoulders of the punch. The stresses and changes in thickness during drawing are summarised in Figure 9.

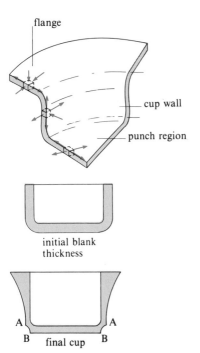

Figure 9 (a) Stresses in a sector of a drawn cup. (b) Change of thickness on a section through a drawn cup (exaggerated); (from Johnson and Mellor, Plasticity for Mechanical Engineers, Van Nostrand).

9

Finally, the middle region in Figure 8 is a narrow annulus, the size of which depends on the clearance between the punch and die. The metal in this region is not bent over the shoulders of either the punch or the die and is subjected to tensile loading throughout. Often the clearance between punch and die exceeds the maximum thickness of the blank on entering the die (10–20% greater), but sometimes it is designed to be otherwise, and in this case there occurs *wall ironing* to give a cup of uniform wall thickness. The prevailing stress during ironing is a radial compression on the metal as it is squeezed between punch and die. Ironing confers the benefits of adding strength to the side wall by work hardening, increasing the depth of the cup for a given blank size, and giving a smooth, burnished finish. It is often carried out as a separate operation (Figure 10). The thin walls achieved in seamless steel or aluminium beer cans are formed in this way.

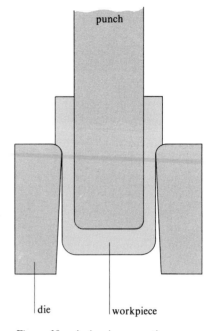

Figure 10   An ironing operation

SAQ 2

What is the hoop strain in the circumference of a circular blank of diameter D_0 when deep drawn by a punch of diameter D_p?

The answer to this question shows that the plastic hoop strain in the rim of the blank increases with the ratio D_0/D_p.

> How would you expect the force required on the punch to vary with the distance travelled by the punch (the 'stroke')?
>
> ___
>
> As the punch moves, elements of material (such as *AB* in Figure 8) are being progressively deformed and you would expect the force to *increase* as the material work-hardens.

The punch force reaches a maximum value as the rim of the blank approaches the die radius and thereafter it falls off. For a given punch size, the maximum punch force increases with the size of the blank (it increases with D_0/D_p); deeper cups require a larger value of D_0/D_p and therefore a larger drawing force.

> Will there therefore be a limit to the depth of cup that can be drawn?
>
> ___
>
> Yes. The punch force is carried by the walls of the cup; as cups get deeper a point will be reached at which the maximum drawing force sets up an axial tensile stress in the walls that exceeds the tensile strength, and the wall will tear.

In practice, the *draw ratio*, D_0/D_p, is limited to values less than about 2.3. The *drawability* of a sheet material is assessed in terms of the maximum draw ratio that can be used without tearing, and the Swift cupping test lays down a set of standard conditions for assessing this. Having a punch of fixed diameter D_p, blanks of increasing diameter are drawn until the largest, $D_{0\,max}$, that can be drawn without fracture is found. Some values of the limiting draw ratio appear in Table 2 for various common materials, including cartridge brass. Apart from the rate of work-hardening (usually expressed by the index n in the empirical equation of the true stress σ–strain ε curve: $\sigma = k\varepsilon^n$), the material property that most affects the drawability is the *average strain ratio* $\bar{R}$, which is defined as:

$$\bar{R} = \frac{1}{4}(R_0 + 2R_{45} + R_{90})$$

where the strain ratio R_i is obtained by carrying out a tensile test on a sheet test-piece cut with its length at an angle i to the rolling direction and measuring the changes in width and thickness:

$$R_i = \frac{\text{width strain}}{\text{thickness strain}}$$

Table 2 Values of drawability and average strain ratio for a range of materials

	maximum blank diameter / cup diameter	$\bar{R}$
aluminium	2.10	0.5
stainless steel	2.15	1.1
mild steel	2.20	1.2
α-brass	2.25	1.1
titanium	2.7	3.7

(Don't confuse this with the 'stress ratio' in Unit 8–9B; unfortunately, the symbol R is in common use for both).

> If the material is isotropic (non-directional) in its properties, what would you expect the value of R_i to be?

> An isotropic material when stretched should contract by equal proportions in *all* transverse directions, including the width and thickness directions, giving $R_i = 1$.

In practice rolled metal sheets are usually anisotropic owing to the development by plastic deformation of some *preferred orientation* among the grains (as opposed to a purely *random* collection of grain orientations). As a result, in rolled fcc or bcc metals the value of $\bar{R}$ can vary from about 0.75 to 2, while in hcp metals, values as high as 5 or 6 are found.

> Which values of $\bar{R}$ (>1 or <1) would you expect to improve the drawability over that of isotropic material?

> During deep-drawing, failure (tearing) is preceded by a thinning down of the material. For a given stretch, a material with larger $\bar{R}$ ($\bar{R} > 1$) thins less than an isotropic material, and so you might expect this material to have better drawability.

In practice, this is found to be true: the drawability improves with the value of $\bar{R}$ (Table 2). Provided it increases $\bar{R}$, anisotropy is favourable, but it sometimes brings a drawback too — the tendency for R_i to vary with the orientation i. As a result the drawn cups have an 'eared' rim which has to be cut off before the cup can be used.

On account of there being a limiting draw ratio, it is not possible to produce, in only one drawing operation, a cup that is much deeper than its diameter. To draw deep cups (like cartridge cases) requires *redrawing* — the use of successive drawing operations (punctuated by annealing). If the material is thick enough, drawing may not require a blank-holder (Figure 11a) but thin material tends to wrinkle so a blank-holder is then used (Figure 11b). If there is clearance between the punch and the cup throughout the operation (i.e. there is no internal support to the walls), little change occurs in the wall thickness and the redrawing is regarded as a *sinking* operation (as opposed to ironing, which was described earlier).

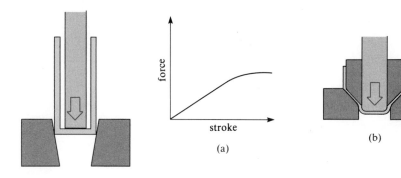

(a)

(b)

Figure 11 Re-drawing operations; (a) no blank-holder is used in this sinking operation; (b) a blank-holder is used to prevent buckling of thin material

2.2 Spinning

For the small-scale manufacture of hollow objects with circular symmetry, such as brass musical instruments, (including klaxon horns!), a spinning operation may be preferred. The workpiece is clamped to a revolving form block, and forced to conform to that shape by pressing a smooth tool against the surface of the workpiece, as illustrated in Figure 12. The tool may be simply a wooden pole with a rounded end controlled manually; this calls for considerable skill by the operator. Alternatively, the tool may be a small-diameter shaped roller. During spinning, the workpiece is plastically deformed by a combination of stretching around, and bending over, the form block.

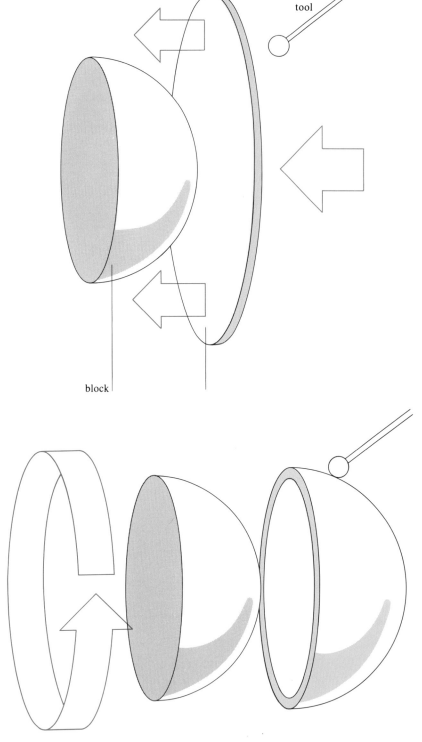

Figure 12   The principle of metal spinning

2.3 Summary

- Cylindrical cups can be drawn from a flat disc of a ductile metal by using a punch and die in a press.

- In the central region of the blank, under the punch, a state of balanced biaxial tension is set up during drawing, which is accompanied by some stretching and thinning of the material. This deformation is usually most severe at the shoulders of the punch.

- In the outer region of the blank, material is subjected to a hoop compression and a radial tension. This radial stress draws the material into the die to form the walls of the cup. To enter the die, the material must contract in the hoop direction and increase in thickness. The hoop compression causes a thin blank to wrinkle and, to suppress this, a blank holder is used.

- As the blank enters the die, it bends plastically as it passes over the die radius and then straightens out again as it forms the wall of the cup.

- In the walls of the cup, drawing sets up a tension along the axis of the cup, a hoop tension and radial compression on the inside wall surface.

- If the clearance between punch and die is less than the blank thickness, *wall ironing* occurs as the wall is squeezed between punch and die.

- The punch force increases as the punch moves, reaching a maximum value as the edge of the blank approaches the die. The maximum force increases with the value of D_0/D_p, the *draw ratio*.

- At a critical value of D_0/D_p, the limiting draw ratio, the punch force exerts an excessive stress on the cup walls and fracture occurs. This restricts the draw ratio to values below about 2.3 and makes redrawing necessary in order to make deep cups.

SAQ 3

For simplicity, materials are sometimes regarded as being 'ideally plastic' (i.e. the stress–strain curve is elastic up to the yield stress and thereafter the strength is constant). Could such a material successfully be deep-drawn?

SAQ 4

Bearing in mind the need to avoid the 'orange-peel' effect, and the requirement for high ductility, recommend a suitable average grain diameter for cartridge brass that is to be deep-drawn.

Now return to the case study, Section 12A:3.

3 Residual stress

In relation to welds in Units 3–6, you saw that a material can be under stress, even when it is free from external forces. Such stresses are usually referred to as 'residual' or 'internal'. Their presence can be critical — indeed, you saw how the existence of residual stress was decisive in causing the explosion of the pressure vessel in Units 3–6. In this section, we will consider how plastic deformation can induce residual stresses in cylindrical components, and we will see how such stresses can be measured in practice. We shall be concerned only with *macroscopic* residual stresses which are significant over distances comparable with the dimensions of the component we are dealing with (as opposed to *microscopic* residual stresses such as those associated with a dislocation or a second phase particle). Also, in deference to the case study, we will deal only with components having cylindrical symmetry. This brings some welcome simplification: σ_r, σ_θ and σ_z (Unit 5B) are *principal* stresses, and because of the symmetry, the principal stresses are all independent of θ and z.

3.1 Examples in cylinders

I want to show you two simple examples of how a pattern of residual stresses can be generated in cylindrical tubes (such as cartridge cases).

3.1.1 A split tube

Suppose we have a thin sheet of metal bent into the form of a short open tube with a small longitudinal gap, as in Figure 13. (Before seamless cartridge cases were invented, cases were made from such tubes by closing the gap and soldering the ends together.) Suppose the tube was well annealed (i.e. it contained no residual stress) prior to closing and soldering. Because the annealed tube contains no internal stress, it also contains no internal bending moments. However, this is no longer true when the ends are brought together by elastic deformation to form a closed tube — there must be a bending moment in the closed tube because if the ends are released, the radius of curvature of the tube will change as the gap springs open again. Applying engineers' bending theory to the tube walls:

$$\frac{M}{I} = \frac{E}{R}$$

or $M = EI\left(\frac{1}{R}\right)$

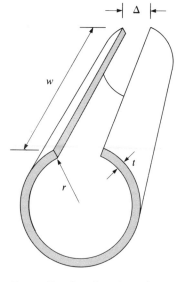

Figure 13 Circular tube with a longitudinal opening

The bending moment M depends inversely on the radius of curvature R of the neutral axis. Our 'beam' (the tube wall) is already curved in the unstressed state, but this doesn't matter because we are concerned with *changes* in the curvature of the wall. When the gap is closed by applying a bending moment to the ends, there is a change δM in the bending moment in the tube wall (from an initial value of zero) where:

$$\delta M = EI\,\delta\left(\frac{1}{R}\right) \tag{1}$$

The *change* in the curvature $\delta\left(\frac{1}{R}\right)$ can be worked out quite easily. From Figure 13, the gap is Δ wide and the radius of the closed tube is r, so the circumference of the open tube is $(2\pi r + \Delta)$ and its radius is therefore

$$\left(\frac{2\pi r + \Delta}{2\pi}\right).$$

It follows that:

$$\delta\left(\frac{1}{R}\right) = \left\{\frac{1}{r} - \frac{2\pi}{(2\pi r + \Delta)}\right\}$$

Putting this into Equation 1 and rearranging we get:

$$\delta M = EI\,\frac{\Delta}{r(2\pi r + \Delta)}$$

$$\doteqdot \frac{EI\Delta}{2\pi r^2} \quad \text{(provided } \Delta \text{ is small compared to } r\text{).}$$

Since the bending moment in the open tube is zero, δM is equal to the residual bending moment M_R when the tube is closed; expressing the second moment of area I in terms of the dimensions of the tube wall

$$\left(I = \frac{wt^3}{12}\right)$$

the last equation becomes:

$$M_R = \frac{Ewt^3\Delta}{24\pi r^2} \tag{2}$$

14

We have assumed that closing the tube involved only *elastic* deformation, so we can relate M_R to the residual stresses σ_R by means of elastic bending theory:

$$\frac{M_R}{I} = \frac{\sigma_R}{y}$$

Rearranging

$$\sigma_R = \frac{M_R y}{I}$$

and recalling Equation 2,

$$\sigma_R = \frac{E\Delta y}{2\pi r^2} \tag{3}$$

where the 'through-thickness' coordinate y varies from $-t/2$ to $t/2$ (t is the wall thickness). The residual stress σ_R is plotted against y in Figure 14. By contemplating this diagram, you can learn an important general principle about residual stresses — they must be *self-equilibrating*. In other words, *on any plane through a component containing residual stress, the total force and the total moment of forces must be zero.*

You can see this by imagining the closed tube to consist of two equal parts held together in equilibrium by the residual stresses (see the free-body diagram in Figure 15). The forces (represented by arrows) must balance to give equilibrium, (zero net force and zero net bending moment). It is clear that they do in this case.

> Given a sample of the closed tube, how could you use it to get a measure of the residual stress in it, based on the foregoing discussion?
>
> ───────────────────────────────
>
> Cut the tube open longitudinally and measure the opening displacement Δ of two marks drawn as close to the cut as possible. Use Equation 2 to calculate the residual bending moment; use Equation 3 to calculate residual stresses, *on the assumption that these vary linearly with distance across the wall.*

Of course, the cut ends might not move apart at all — they might move *together* (Figure 16), giving a negative value of Δ. This just means the residual bending moment has the opposite sign to that considered above.

Unfortunately, in practice residual stresses do not often have such a simple distribution as this, as the next example will show. The distribution of residual stress with position is usually non-linear and unknown, so while the inferred value of M_R is valid, that of σ_R is based on the sweeping assumption of a linear distribution.

3.1.2 A pressure vessel after yielding

One of the most important causes of residual stress is *plastic deformation*; *residual stresses are left behind whenever a component undergoes non-uniform plastic deformation by cold-working.*

In Unit 5B Section 4.2, you studied the stresses in the walls of pressurised cylinders; you saw that as the pressure within a thick-walled vessel is progressively increased, yielding (according to the Tresca criterion) begins at the bore and spreads radially until it reaches the external diameter, when there is a state of general yielding. For an ideal plastic material, this requires an internal pressure;

$$p_Y = \sigma_Y \ln k \tag{4}$$

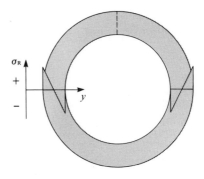

Figure 14   Residual stress σ_R as a function of distance y across the wall when the tube in Figure 13 has been closed up by elastic deformation

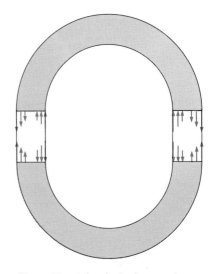

Figure 15   A free-body diagram for two halves of the tube in Figure 14

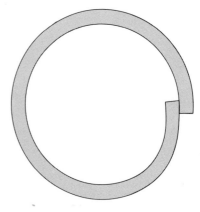

Figure 16   The relaxed shape of a cut tube when the residual bending moment has the opposite sense of that in Figure 14

Now I want to examine the state of stress that remains in the cylinder walls after this pressure has been removed. I shall assume that all the deformation occurring during unloading is elastic. I can use the principle of superposition of stress: the residual stress at a given point in the cylinder after pressurising and unloading is simply the sum of two stresses:

(i) the stress at that point in the pressurised vessel;

(ii) the stress at that point in an identical vessel deformed elastically by an internal 'pressure' of $(-p_Y)$, as sketched in Figure 17.

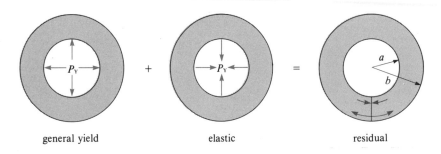

general yield   elastic   residual

Figure 17   Superposition of two stress states to get the residual stress

The stresses in case (i) can be recalled from Unit 5B, Section 4.2, where the radial stress in a fully yielded cylinder was stated to be:

$$\sigma_r = \sigma_Y \ln \frac{r}{b} \tag{5}$$

Since yielding is occurring at all points, we have:

$$\sigma_\theta - \sigma_r = \sigma_Y \tag{6}$$

which, combined with Equation 5 gives:

$$\sigma_\theta = \sigma_Y \left(1 + \ln \frac{r}{b}\right) \tag{7}$$

Similarly, expressions for the radial and hoop stresses in an elastically deformed vessel can be recalled from Unit 5B (SAQ 17); they are:

$$\sigma_r = \frac{p}{k^2 - 1} \left(1 - \frac{b^2}{r^2}\right) \tag{7}$$

$$\sigma_\theta = \frac{p}{k^2 - 1} \left(1 + \frac{b^2}{r^2}\right) \tag{8}$$

In this case the pressure p is $(-p_Y)$, where p_Y is given by Equation 4. Making this substitution for p, the residual radial stress σ_{rR} is simply the sum of Equations 5 and 7:

$$\sigma_{rR} = \sigma_Y \left\{\ln \frac{r}{b} - \frac{\ln k}{k^2 - 1} \left(1 - \frac{b^2}{r^2}\right)\right\} \tag{9}$$

Similarly, by adding Equations 7 and 8 we get the residual hoop stress:

$$\sigma_{\theta R} = \sigma_Y \left\{1 + \ln \frac{r}{b} - \frac{\ln k}{k^2 - 1} \left(1 + \frac{b^2}{r^2}\right)\right\} \tag{10}$$

These residual stresses are plotted in Figure 18 as a function of radial position r for a cylinder with $k = \dfrac{b}{a} = 2$, and you can see that every-where they are less than the yield stress; this is physically necessary — residual stresses cannot exceed the yield strength without being relieved by secondary yielding. Note that the distribution of residual stress is not linear with r in either case; note too how the stresses are self-equilibrating; for example the total force is zero on any radial plane (in other words, the two shaded areas in Figure 18 are equal). Finally, note that the residual

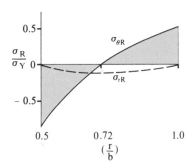

Figure 18   The variation of radial (σ_{rR}) and hoop ($\sigma_{\theta R}$) residual stresses with the radial distance across the wall for a cylindrical vessel with $k = \dfrac{b}{a} = 2$, when unloaded after general yielding

hoop stress is *compressive* at the *inside* surface of the vessel, which is where a *tensile* plastic hoop strain first occurred on yielding. This makes a general point about residual stresses: the *sign* of the residual stress at a given place is usually *opposite* to that of the plastic strain at that place (relative to the *average* strain).

SAQ 5

An annealed brass tube of external diameter 19.3 mm and internal diameter 16.88 mm is pressurised until it yields throughout. Plot a graph of the distribution of the residual hoop stress across the wall when the tube is unloaded. If the tube was cut longitudinally at one point, what would be the displacement of the cut ends? Take $\sigma_Y = 100$ MN m^{-2}, $E = 100$ GN m^{-2} and

$$\int x \ln x \, dx = \frac{x^2}{2}\left(\ln x - \frac{1}{2}\right)$$

and

$$\int \ln x \, dx = x \ln x - x.$$

3.2 Measurement of residual stresses

It is not my intention to review all the known methods of measuring residual stresses — there is neither time nor space. I shall confine my attention to mechanical methods that are applicable to cylindrical objects like cartridge cases.

If we wished to measure an *applied* stress by mechanical means, we might tackle it by one of the methods described in Section 2B : 2. For example, we might attach a strain gauge rosette to the point of interest on the unloaded component, measure the strain that occurs on loading and from this infer what the stresses are (assuming that deformation is elastic and using the elastic stress–strain relations). In other words, we measure stress by *comparing* the stressed and unstressed states. So too with residual stresses, except that we start with the material already stressed. To get the comparison, we must somehow release the residual stress and we do this by cutting into the material, thereby creating new surfaces. Since no force can act perpendicularly to a *free* surface, the residual stresses normal to these surfaces are released by cutting. The release of these stresses unbalances the pattern of residual stresses in the remaining material, causing it to strain elastically in order to establish a balance again. By measuring this strain, the stresses released can be inferred. Let's look at an example.

3.2.1 Heyn method

A simple method for determining the residual longitudinal stress in a cylinder was used as early as 1911 expressly for the purpose of investigating internal stresses in extruded brass rods which exhibited season-cracking. The method involves machining away the surface layer (the 'skin') and measuring the resulting longitudinal strain ε in the rod. Suppose that the average longitudinal stress $\bar{\sigma}_s$ in the skin is tensile; this arises because the core exerts a tensile force P_s on the skin, and so conversely the skin must exert an equal *compressive* force P_c on the core.

What will happen to the length of the core when the skin is removed?

It will *extend* due to the removal of the compressive force applied by the skin.

Referring to Figure 19, the cross-sectional area of the skin is $dA_1 = (A_0 - A_1)$, so

$$P_s = \bar{\sigma}_s \, dA_1$$

If the longitudinal strain in the core caused by removing the skin is $d\varepsilon_1$, then

$$P_c = -A_1 E d\varepsilon_1$$

(the negative sign means that P_c is compressive). Putting $P_s = -P_c$ we get:

$$\bar{\sigma}_s \, dA_1 = A_1 E d\varepsilon_1$$

or in words:

$$\left(\begin{array}{c} \textit{force acting on skin} \\ \textit{before removal} \end{array}\right) = \left(\begin{array}{c} \textit{change in force acting on core} \\ \textit{when skin is removed} \end{array}\right)$$

hence

$$\bar{\sigma}_s = \frac{A_1 E d\varepsilon_1}{dA_1} \tag{11}$$

This is rather a crude analysis, since it gives the longitudinal residual stress only if it is distributed as shown in Figure 20a, whereas in reality there will be a continuously varying stress profile across the diameter of the bar (Figure 20b).

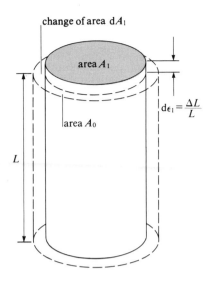

Figure 19   In the Heyn method, the outside 'skin' is removed from a circular bar and the resulting change in length ΔL is measured

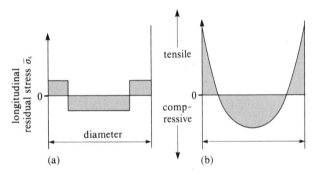

(a) (b)

Figure 20   Variations in longitudinal residual stress across the diameter of a bar of (a) idealised, (b) a more likely, distribution

In order to achieve a more accurate determination of the stress pattern, a series of thin annular volumes must be shaved off, and the change in length of the remaining rod measured each time. Equation 11 gives the true value of the stress existing in the surface skin, but for successive layers, the equation must be modified to take account of the redistribution of stress in the remaining bar. When the first skin is removed, the core extends by $d\varepsilon_1$ and the stress in the second skin has then been altered from its original value by $E d\varepsilon_1$; when the second skin is removed the stress in it is (according to Equation 11)

$$\frac{A_2 E d\varepsilon_2}{dA_2};$$

so the *original* value of the stress in the second skin was (before the removal of any layers);

$$\bar{\sigma}_2 = \frac{A_2 E d\varepsilon_2}{dA_2} - E d\varepsilon_1$$

where A_2 is the core area when two layers have been removed and dA_2 is the area of the second layer. Extending the argument to n layers, the original stress in the nth layer was:

$$\bar{\sigma}_n = \frac{A_n E d\varepsilon_n}{dA_n} - E(d\varepsilon_1 + d\varepsilon_2 + \dots d\varepsilon_{n-1})$$

As the area of the layers tends towards zero, this can be written as:

$$\sigma_{zR}(r) = E\left(A\frac{d\varepsilon}{dA} - \int d\varepsilon\right)$$

$$= E\left(A\frac{d\varepsilon}{dA} - \varepsilon\right) \tag{12}$$

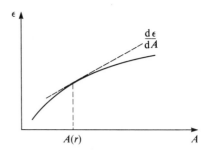

Figure 21 *The measured longitudinal strain ε plotted against the cross-sectional area A of the bar*

where $\sigma_{zR}(r)$ is the longitudinal residual stress at any radial position r in the specimen. To evaluate this for a given value of r (and its corresponding value of A, $A(r)$), the axial strain is plotted against A for successive layers, and the slope of the curve, $\dfrac{d\varepsilon}{dA}$, is obtained for that radial position within the bar, as shown in Figure 21. This is then used in Equation 12 to give the value of $\sigma_{zR}(r)$.

Can you think of a major shortcoming of this analysis?

It ignores the possible existence of residual hoop and radial stresses. Removal of layers would remove these stresses as well as the longitudinal stress and their effect should be taken into account.

Although the Heyn method is wrong to ignore these other stresses, I have presented it because the line of argument it employs is valid and it is extended to take account of all three components of residual stress in the next method.

3.2.2 The Sachs method*

This approach can be used to determine all three principal residual stresses (hoop, radial, and longitudinal) in cylindrically symmetrical components such as tubes or bars.

The component is bored out (either mechanically or chemically) in small increments and after each increment, the changes in length and outside diameter are measured to give axial and hoop strains, ε_z and ε_θ respectively, on the outside surface. Alternatively, these strains can be measured directly with strain gauges (Figure 22). This is similar in principle to the Heyn method except that the layers are being stripped off the inside surface rather than the outside, and the hoop strain of the outside surface is monitored in addition to the longitudinal strain. I shall now derive expressions for the residual stresses in terms of the measured strains ε_θ and ε_z. You will *not* be asked to repeat these derivations in assessment or examination questions, but you will be expected to *recognise* and use the expressions when they are quoted and you will be expected to know the *principles* that were used in their derivation.

Axial stress

The expression for the residual axial stress σ_{zR} is found as follows. The outside (free) surface (where the strains are being measured) is under *plane stress* so when an increment of area dA is removed from the bore of area A, the released forces cause a change in axial stress $\Delta\sigma_z$ at the surface, where:

$$d\sigma_z = \frac{E}{1 - v^2}d(\varepsilon_z + v\varepsilon_\theta) \quad \text{(equation for } \sigma_1 \text{ in Table 4, Unit 2B)}$$

$$= E'\,d\Lambda \quad \left(\text{representing } (\varepsilon_z + v\varepsilon_\theta) \text{ by } \Lambda \text{ and } \frac{E}{1 - v^2} \text{ by } E'\right)$$

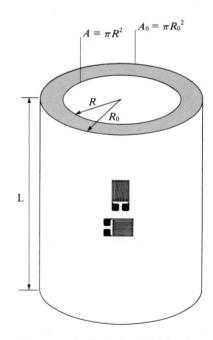

Figure 22 *In the Sachs method, a thin annulus is removed from the bore of a tube, and the resulting changes in length and diameter (or circumference) are measured on the outside of the tube*

* *Zeitschrift für Metallkunde* (1927) Vol. 19 pages 352–357.

The corresponding change in longitudinal force on the remaining area $(A_0 - A)$ is $d\sigma_z (A_0 - A)$ or $E' \, d\Lambda (A_0 - A)$ (taking $d\sigma_z$ to be constant over the cross-section). As in the Heyn method, this is equal to the longitudinal force (before boring out) acting on the layer, area dA: $\sigma_z(A) \, dA$, where $\sigma_z(A)$ is the longitudinal stress in the removed layer before boring-out.

Balancing these two forces:

$$\sigma_z(A) \, dA = E' \, d\Lambda(A_0 - A)$$

or

$$\sigma_z(A) = \frac{E' \, d\Lambda(A_0 - A)}{dA}$$

As the area of the increment $dA \rightarrow 0$,

$$\sigma_z(A) = E'(A_0 - A)\frac{d\Lambda}{dA}$$

The *total* change in longitudinal stress $\Delta\sigma_z$ due to boring out all earlier increments is:

$$\Delta\sigma_z = \int d\sigma_z = \int E' \, d\Lambda = E'\Lambda$$

The *original* value of the residual longitudinal stress at that radial position is:

$$\sigma_{zR}(A) = \sigma_z(A) - \Delta\sigma_z$$

$$= E'\left\{(A_0 - A)\frac{d\Lambda}{dA} - \Lambda\right\} \qquad (13)$$

This is similar to Equation 12 with ε replaced by Λ and the area A by $(A_0 - A)$. It is evaluated in the same way by plotting a graph of Λ against A and finding the slope at chosen values of A.

Could the longitudinal residual stress be constant across the wall of a tube?

Only if it were zero. It can't have a constant finite value because that would require a cross-section of the tube to carry a net force. Equilibrium demands that the total force should be zero.

The longitudinal residual stress would have to have both positive and negative values, such as those shown in Figure 23. The difference between these three types of distribution becomes clear if a thin-walled tube is cut to form a longitudinal tongue (Figure 24).

In which direction would the end of the tongue move for each of the stress distributions shown in Figure 23?

The tongue would deform in such a way as to relax the axial stresses. So in case (a) the tongue would bend, concave side towards the centre of the tube — the end would move *inwards*. In case (b) the tongue will bend the opposite way, its end moving *outwards* (as in Figure 24). In case (c), the end of the tongue would not move at all (there is no bending moment to release).

Radial stress

Consider a specimen in the form of a thick-walled cylinder containing a residual radial stress $\sigma_r(A)$ at a radial distance r which encloses an area A.

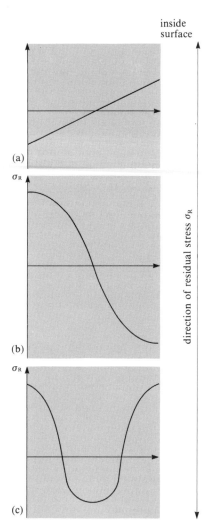

Figure 23 *Three possible distributions of longitudinal residual stress across the wall of a tube*

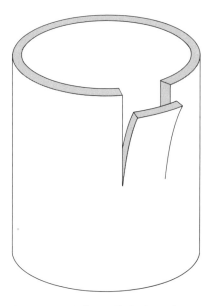

Figure 24 *A thin-walled tube with two longitudinal cuts, forming a 'tongue'*

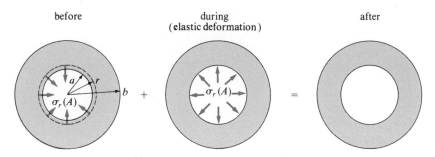

before   during
         (elastic deformation)   after

Figure 25   Superposition of radial stresses at a circumference of radius r; before boring out, the radial stress is $\sigma_r(A)$ but this is relaxed to zero when the tube is bored out. The elastic deformation of the tube that occurs during boring out is that which would be caused by application of a pressure $\sigma_r(a)$

What happens to this radial stress when the bore is drilled out to a cross-sectional area A?

The radial stress falls to zero because a free surface is formed. The radial stress *changes* by $-\sigma_r(A)$.

When this stress is released, the specimen deforms elastically in order to re-establish equilibrium. According to the superposition principle (Figure 25) the deformation is that which would be caused by applying an internal *pressure* of $\sigma_r(A)$; suppose that the hoop strain is ε_θ and the axial strain is ε_z on the outside surface of the tube (where the strain gauges are). Since the surface is under plane stress, the elastic deformation of the tube is accompanied by a change in hoop stress at the surface of:

$$\Delta\sigma_\theta(A_0) = \frac{E}{1-v^2}(\varepsilon_\theta + v\varepsilon_z) \qquad \text{(Table 4, Unit 2B)}$$

For brevity, let's define

$$\Theta = \varepsilon_\theta + v\varepsilon_z$$

Therefore

$$\Delta\sigma_\theta(A_0) = E'\Theta \qquad (14)$$

This change in hoop stress can also be obtained another way — from the Lamé equations. As you saw in Unit 5B, these equations describe the stresses in a thick-walled cylinder:

$$\sigma_r(r) = A - \frac{B}{r^2}$$

At the outside (free) surface, $r = b$, and $\sigma_r(b) = 0$, so:

$$0 = A - \frac{B}{b^2}$$

or $$A = \frac{B}{b^2} \qquad (15)$$

Therefore the hoop stress is:

$$\sigma_\theta(r) = A + \frac{B}{r^2}$$

$$= B\left(\frac{1}{b^2} + \frac{1}{r^2}\right)$$

At the outside surface, $r = b$, so:

$$\sigma_\theta(b) = \frac{2B}{b^2}$$

This is an alternative expression for the change in hoop stress that occurs at the outside surface when the tube deforms (on boring out), so it can be put equal to Equation 14:

$$\frac{2B}{b^2} = E'\,\Theta$$

or $\qquad B = E'\,\Theta b^2 / 2 \qquad\qquad\qquad$ (16)

The elastic deformation of the (outer) cylinder that occurs during boring-out is equivalent to that caused by applying a pressure p of $\sigma_r(A)$ to the bore (see Figure 25); from the Lamé equation for the radial stress:

$$-p = -\sigma_r(A)$$

$$= A - \frac{B}{r^2}$$

$$= B\left(\frac{1}{b^2} - \frac{1}{r^2}\right) \qquad \text{(from Equation 15)}$$

$$= \frac{E'\Theta b^2}{2}\left(\frac{1}{b^2} - \frac{1}{r^2}\right) \qquad \text{(from Equation 16)}$$

$$= \frac{E'\Theta}{2}\left(1 - \frac{b^2}{r^2}\right)$$

$$= \frac{E'\Theta}{2}\left(1 - \frac{A_0}{A}\right)$$

In other words, the residual stress is:

$$\sigma_{rR}(A) = \frac{E'\Theta}{2}\left(\frac{A_0}{A} - 1\right) \qquad\qquad (17)$$

This is relatively easy to evaluate at any chosen value of A — it depends simply on the value of the strain Θ at that stage of boring out.

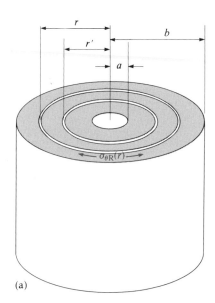

(a)

Hoop stress

Consider Figure 26b and suppose that a small increment of radius r is removed in which the hoop stress just prior to removal was $\sigma_\theta(r)$. This increment is essentially a thin-walled tube in which there is the usual relation between the hoop and radial stress (i.e. the 'pressure' within the tube):

$$\sigma_\theta(r) = \frac{d\sigma_r(r)r}{dr} \qquad\qquad (18)$$

The right-hand side is similar to Equation 7, Unit 3–6B, with the wall thickness t being dr in this case, and $d\sigma_r(r)$ being the change in radial stress across the thickness of the 'tube'.

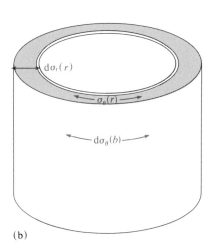

(b)

Drilling out the increment creates a free surface with radius $(r + dr)$ across which the radial stress is zero. Drilling out has changed this radial stress by $-d\sigma_r(r)$. Recalling the equations for the principal stresses in a thick cylinder (SAQ 17, Units 3–6B) we can write:

$$\sigma_r(r) = \frac{Pa^2}{(b^2 - a^2)}\left(\frac{r^2 - b^2}{r^2}\right)$$

and $\qquad \sigma_\theta(r) = \dfrac{Pa^2}{(b^2 - a^2)}\left(\dfrac{r^2 + b^2}{r^2}\right)$

So $\qquad \sigma_\theta(b) = \dfrac{2Pa^2}{b^2 - a^2}$

$$= \frac{2r^2\sigma_r(r)}{(r^2 - b^2)}$$

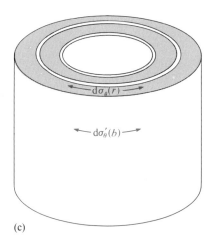

(c)

Figure 26 A hypothetical change in hoop stress across the wall of a tube that occurs when the tube is bored out by a small amount dr

In this case, we are dealing with *changes* in stress, so the change in hoop stress on the outside surface of the specimen corresponding to a change in radial stress of $(-d\sigma_r(r))$ at radius r is:

$$d\sigma_\theta(b) = \frac{2r^2(-d\sigma_r(r))}{(r^2 - b^2)}$$

Recalling Equation 18,

$$d\sigma_\theta(b) = \frac{2r\sigma_\theta(r)\,dr}{b^2 - r^2}$$

This can also be written in terms of the strains measured on the outside surface (Equation 14):

$$d\sigma_\theta(b) = E'\,d\Theta$$

Equating the last two equations and rearranging, we get:

$$\sigma_\theta(r) = E'\frac{(b^2 - r^2)}{2r\,dr}\,d\Theta$$

But $A = \pi r^2$ and $A_0 = \pi b^2$

so $dA = 2\pi r\,dr$

and $\sigma_\theta(r) = E'(A_0 - A)\dfrac{d\Theta}{dA}$

This expression gives the hoop stress at radius r, just prior to drilling out an increment of radius r. However, this stress has been affected by removing all the previous increments of smaller radius such as r' (Figure 26c). When an increment of radius r' is removed, there occurs a change in the hoop stress at the outer surface, $d\sigma_\theta'(b)$, and a corresponding change at radius r, $d\sigma_\theta(r)$; these stress changes are related by the expression for hoop stress in a thick cylinder:

$$\sigma_\theta(r) = \frac{Pa^2}{b^2 - a^2}\left(\frac{r^2 + b^2}{r^2}\right)$$

So $\quad d\sigma_\theta(r) = \dfrac{d\sigma_\theta'(b)}{2}\left(\dfrac{r^2 + b^2}{r^2}\right)$

$$= E'\,d\Theta\left(\frac{r^2 + b^2}{2r^2}\right)$$

$$= E'\,d\Theta\left(\frac{A + A_0}{2A}\right)$$

The *total* change in hoop stress at radius r due to removing *all* such increments (those with radius r' between a and r) is:

$$\Delta\sigma_\theta(r) = \int d\sigma_\theta(r) = E'\left(\frac{A + A_0}{2A}\right)\int d\Theta$$

$$= E'\left(\frac{A + A_0}{2A}\right)\Theta$$

If the *original* hoop stress at radius r was $\sigma_{\theta R}(r)$, we have:

$$\sigma_{\theta R}(r) = \sigma_\theta(r) - \Delta\sigma_\theta(r)$$

$$= E'\left\{(A_0 - A)\frac{d\Theta}{dA} - \frac{(A + A_0)}{2A}\Theta\right\} \qquad (20)$$

To evaluate this at any radial position r, we plot a graph of the measured strain Θ against the bored-out area, and determine the slope $\dfrac{d\Theta}{dA}$ at $A(r)$, rather like we did earlier in Figure 21.

3.2.3 An example

As an example of the application of the Sachs method, I am going to cite the work of B. J. Meadows who measured the residual hoop stress set up in tubes of 70/30 brass. He took lengths of annealed tube with an outside diameter of 1 inch and a wall thickness of 0.056 inch, and reduced the outside diameter by various amounts by sinking. His measured residual hoop stresses, shown in Figure 27, show a roughly linear distribution across the wall; they increase with the reduction in diameter of the tube and reach a maximum tensile value at a small distance beneath the outside surface, and a roughly equal maximum compressive value at the bore.

If a length of this tube was cut longitudinally, what would happen to its ends?

They would move apart. The tension at the outside surface would relax towards zero and in so doing, the outside circumference would shrink. Conversely, the bore would expand causing the ends to bend outwards.

You will be able to investigate for yourself the residual hoop stress in brass tube when you come to do Home Experiment 5 in the case study.

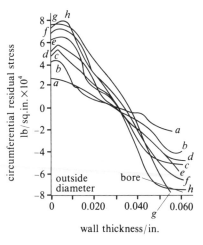

Figure 27   (Curve h) Distribution of residual hoop stress in a tube sunk from an initial diameter of one inch to one of 0.701 inch (from B. J. Meadows, 'The Influence of Cold-Drawing on the Magnitude and Distribution of Residual Circumferential Stresses in 70/30 Brass Tube'; Journal of the Institute of Metals, Vol. 93, pages 353–357, 1964–5)

3.3 Summary

- If a thin-walled cylinder is cut longitudinally, and the cut ends move by a distance Δ relative to one another, this indicates that, prior to cutting, the cylinder contained a residual bending moment M_R and residual hoop stresses, where

$$M_R = \frac{EI\Delta}{2\pi r^2}.$$

- A system of residual stresses must be self-equilibrating—there must be no net force and no net moment across any plane in the component.

- Residual stresses arise when a material undergoes non-uniform plastic deformation by cold-working.

- Residual stresses cannot significantly exceed the yield stress.

- Residual stresses can be measured by detaching thin layers from a cylindrical component. This removes the stresses in the layers and unbalances the forces within the remaining component. Equilibrium is restored by the component undergoing a deformation (which is usually elastic).

- In the Sachs method, a cylindrical component is bored-out in small increments, and after each increment, the hoop and axial strains are measured on the outside surface. The residual stresses at a radial position enclosing an area A are given by these expressions:

$$\sigma_{zR}(A) = E' \left\{ (A_0 - A) \frac{d\Lambda}{dA} - \Lambda \right\}$$

$$\sigma_{rR}(A) = \frac{E'\Theta}{2} \left(\frac{A_0}{A} - 1 \right)$$

$$\sigma_{\theta R}(A) = E' \left\{ (A_0 - A) \frac{d\Theta}{dA} - \frac{(A + A_0)}{2A} \Theta \right\}$$

where

$$E' = \frac{E}{1 - v^2}, \Lambda = \varepsilon_z + v\varepsilon_\theta \text{ and } \Theta = \varepsilon_\theta + v\varepsilon_z.$$

You will be expected to be able to recognise and use these equations when they are quoted to you, but you will not be required to derive them.

SAQ 6

If a sample of the tube referred to in Figure 27 with outside diameter 0.701 inch and wall thickness 0.060 inch was cut longitudinally, what would the mutual displacement of the cut ends be? (Hint: approximate the stress distribution in Figure 27 to a linear one; take $E = 100\,\mathrm{GN\,m^{-2}}$ and work in metric units.)

SAQ 7

Residual stresses are induced by shrink-fitting two components together. Consider the steel tubes shown in Figure 28 and suppose that at ambient temperature the outer radius of the smaller one is 0.1 mm greater than the inner radius of the larger cylinder. By heating the larger tube sufficiently it can be fitted over the smaller one.

Calculate the residual stresses (hoop and radial components) in the assembled tubes when they have cooled to ambient temperature. State any assumptions made. (Hint: take the mismatch in hoop strains at the interface to be $\varepsilon_{\theta2} - \varepsilon_{\theta1} = \dfrac{0.1}{150}$; $E = 200\,\mathrm{GN\,m^{-2}}$; $\sigma_z = 0$.)

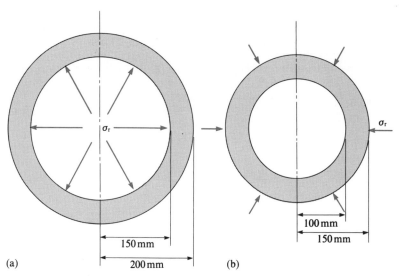

Figure 28 Components to be joined by a shrink fit; (a) outer cylinder; (b) inner cylinder

1 Revision of electrochemistry

In this case study, we are dealing with metals in contact with aqueous (water-containing) environments. In this section I am going to review the factors which affect the response of a metal to these surroundings. The *electrical potential* which a metal develops when immersed in a conducting solution is as central to its response as, say, temperature is to the response of an alloy to heat treatment. You learnt in T252 that a metal would be inert (*immune*), would dissolve freely (*corrode*), or would form a stable, protective oxide film (*passivate*), depending on the value of this potential. But how and why does the potential vary with the composition of the environment, with alloying, or with the presence of cracks and crevices?

1.1 Electrode potentials

The aims of this section are twofold:

(i)   to revise your understanding of electrode potentials and the electrochemical series, and;

(ii)   to demonstrate quantitatively how electrode potentials vary according to reaction conditions.

Cast your mind back to the second level Materials course, T252, and in particular to those units concerned with corrosion (Units 13 and 14). You should recall that corrosion was described there as an electrochemical process and this applies no less to the environmental (or more precisely *chemical*) aspect of stress corrosion cracking.

SAQ 8   (Revision)

Figure 29 represents a piece of steel in an aerated, aqueous environment. Demonstrate for yourself that you are familiar with the elementary terminology of corrosion cells by completing the labels in the diagram. What is the overall chemical equation for the reaction?

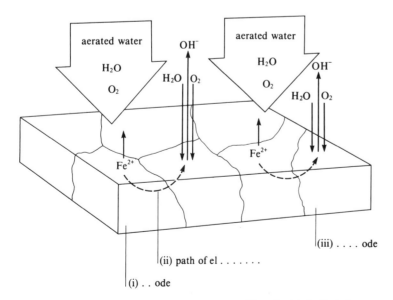

Figure 29   A sketch of the dissolution process; fill in the labels (i)–(iii)

SAQ 9 (*Revision*)

What is understood by the term *electrode potential* and how does it arise in practice?

SAQ 10 (*Revision*)

What is the *electrochemical series*?

SAQ 11 (*Revision*)

Figure 30 is taken from Unit 13, T252; assume that the sulphate solutions each contain a molar solution of metal ions. What is the 'open circuit' voltage between the two metal electrodes?

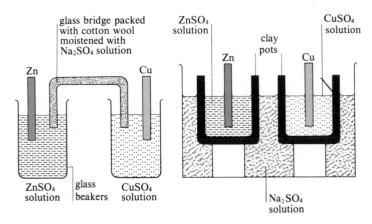

Figure 30   Two cells, each made up of two half (standard) cells. Take the standard electrode potential of zinc and copper to be −0.76 V and 0.34 V, respectively

1.1.1 Effect of concentration

The *standard electrode potentials* quoted in Table 2 of T252, Unit 13 are referred to as 'standard' because they are a set of equilibrium values taken at 298 K with the metal immersed in a molar solution of its own ions. In practice, of course, such conditions rarely apply and so it is necessary to be able to calculate electrode potentials under non-standard conditions, especially those involving changes in concentration of dissolved ions. Such a correction may be carried out by means of the **Nernst equation** which relates the standard electrode potential to the electrode potential under non-standard conditions as follows:

$$E = E_0 + \frac{RT}{nF} \ln C \tag{21}$$

where E is the electrode potential in a solution of concentration C (in moles per litre) and

   E_0 is the standard electrode potential;
   R is the gas constant (8.314 J K^{-1} mole^{-1});
   T is the absolute temperature;
   n is the ionic charge (in multiples of the electronic charge);
   F is the Faraday, 96 500 coulombs.

Simplifying, and assuming a temperature of 291 K, we have

$$E = E_0 + \frac{0.058}{n} \log_{10} C \tag{22}$$

or for a doubly-charged species,

$$E = E_0 + 0.029 \log_{10} C$$

SAQ 12

If the standard electrode potential for the process:

$$Cu^{2+} + 2e^- \rightarrow Cu$$

is $+0.34$ V, calculate the electrode potential that would be measured for a copper rod immersed in a non-standard solution of copper ions, given an initial cupric ion concentration of 10^{-6} moles per litre.

SAQ 13

Having carried out the calculation in SAQ 12, is the copper rod in that example more or less noble than in the standard case?

In a similar manner, the potential of the hydrogen electrode will change according to prevailing conditions. You will recall that the standard hydrogen electrode used as the reference point in compiling the electrochemical series is based on the equilibrium established between hydrogen and a solution of hydrogen ions thus:

$$2H^+ + 2e^- \rightleftharpoons H_2 \uparrow$$

So as the concentration of hydrogen ions (or pH) changes, so will the potential of this electrode.

Using the Nernst equation, obtain a simple expression relating the variation in potential of the hydrogen electrode with change in pH.

From the Nernst equation we have

$$E = E_0 + \frac{0.058}{n} \log_{10} C$$

In this case, $n = 1$ and, by definition, $pH = -\log_{10} C$. E_0 is defined as zero hence $E = -0.058\,pH$ and the potential of the hydrogen electrode decreases in a linear fashion with increase in pH in just the same way that the potential of the copper rod in SAQ 13 decreased with decreased copper concentration.

We can depict this 'concentration effect' graphically, by using a simple potential–pH diagram, (Figure 31).

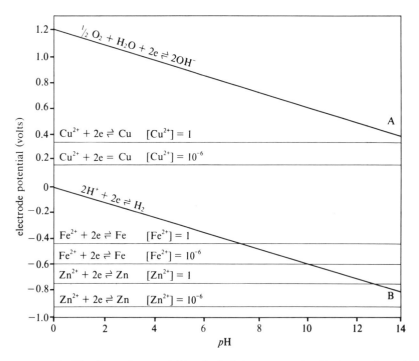

Figure 31   *The electrode potential in volts (relative to a standard hydrogen electrode) as a function of pH for various reactions*

Note that iron and zinc have been included as metals whose corrosion is often of interest, and also the equilibrium slope for the oxygen reduction reaction has been added. Note that the potentials of the metal electrodes are independent of pH and that the slopes of the lines referring to the hydrogen evolution reaction (line B) and the oxygen reduction reaction (line A) are the same.

> Under what conditions would you expect copper to corrode in sulphuric acid at $pH = 1$?
>
> ----
>
> For copper to dissolve it must become the *anode* and for this to happen its potential must lie *below* that of the cathode reaction in Figure 31. The potential of copper does *not* lie below that of the hydrogen reaction (line B) so this cannot be the cathode reaction, but it *does* lie below line A, so copper will dissolve in acid in the presence of oxygen which acts as the cathodic reactant.

However, for other metals the oxygen reduction reaction is not the only possible counter-balancing reaction to metal dissolution at the anode. The possibility of hydrogen evolution also exists when the metal's potential lies below the bound of line B. These two reactions (the reduction of oxygen and the discharge of hydrogen ions) are the most important cathodic reactions responsible for the stimulation of corrosion processes in many situations.

The lines A and B define the 'zone of stability' of water: the limits of potential and pH *outside* of which we may expect to observe the evolution of oxygen (line A) at an electrode acting as an anode or the evolution of hydrogen (line B) at an electrode acting as a cathode (as in the electrolysis of water).

In everyday environments, the corrosion of iron and steel normally takes place accompanied by oxygen reduction, not by hydrogen evolution. Figure 31 suggests that at up to pH 7 (neutral solution) hydrogen evolution would be favoured.

> Can you suggest an explanation for this apparent anomaly?
>
> ----
>
> Remember that Figure 31 is only an *equilibrium diagram*, which does not allow for any flow of current. By definition, all active corrosion processes are not equilibrium processes; a current is flowing.

An important consequence of this lack of equilibrium is that the potential of the metal may not be that shown in Figure 31, due to the effect of polarisation — the topic of the next section.

1.1.2 Summary

- The Nernst equation

$$E = E_0 + \frac{RT}{nF} \log C$$

  is used to obtain non-standard values of electrode potential for a metal in the presence of a concentration C (moles per litre) of its own ions.

- A potential/pH diagram can be used to decide whether a given anodic dissolution reaction will take place, and the nature of the corresponding cathodic reaction.

Note that there is a relation between the concentration of hydrogen ions C_H and that of hydroxyl ions, C_{OH}, arising from the equilibrium between them according to the reaction:

$$H_2O \rightleftharpoons H^+ + OH^-$$

The relation is: $C_H C_{OH} = 10^{-14}$

So, taking logs:

$$\log_{10} C_H + \log_{10} C_{OH} = -14$$

but by definition

$$pH = -\log_{10} C_H$$

and

$$pOH = -\log_{10} C_{OH}$$

so

$$pH + pOH = 14 \qquad (23)$$

Therefore the value of pH indicates the concentration of OH ions and this allows us to plot line A for the oxygen reaction on an E/pH graph.

1.2 Polarisation

If a piece of zinc is immersed in distilled water, it loses a certain number of atoms from the surface, each atom converting to a zinc cation and leaving behind two free electrons in the metal. This process goes on only so far, of course, because the build up of negative (electronic) charge on the metal exerts a restraining influence on the escape of positive ions, until at some point the rate of ionisation from the surface is exactly balanced by the rate of reaction in the opposite direction (reduction of Zn^{2+} ions to Zn metal atoms). The electrode surface is then the site of a net displacement of electrical charge (as in an electrical condenser, Figure 32). This build-up of charge leads to the setting up of a reversible electrode potential.

We are more interested in the case where the metal is an electrode of a cell in which current is flowing; since this is not in equilibrium, its electrode potential differs from the standard value; this change in potential is called *polarisation*.

There are two aims of this section:

(i)   to introduce you to *concentration polarisation* and *activation polarisation*, and

(ii) to demonstrate that kinetic factors associated with these two phenomena can have an important effect on rates of corrosion in practice.

1.2.1 Concentration polarisation

In T252, Unit 13 and the associated summer school activity you saw that in active corrosion processes polarisation effects are very important, sometimes dominant. You should recall polarisation plots of the type shown in Figure 33.

> **SAQ 14** (*Revision*)
> How should the two axes in Figure 33 be labelled, and what do the symbols E_A, E_C, E_{CORR} and i_{CORR} refer to?

> **SAQ 15** (*Revision*)
> Why, in Figure 33, is E_{CORR} so far displaced towards the open circuit anode potential?

There is a good example of one type of polarisation known as *concentration polarisation*. In addition to its presence in corrosion, this effect is found in dry cell batteries and in electrolysis.

In T252 Unit 13 you were introduced to the idea of differential aeration cells arising from variations in the concentration of oxygen at a corroding metal surface. This is a case where the rate of corrosion is controlled by the rate of diffusion of reactants to (or from) the reaction. The electro-chemical considerations can be appreciated by reference to the following cell, where initially both copper electrodes are at the same potential:

$$Cu \mid CuSO_4 \text{ solution} \mid Cu$$

When an external voltage is applied from a battery, it causes copper to dissolve from the anode and to deposit at the cathode. If we vigorously stirred the solution, an ammeter in the circuit would indicate quite a large current flow for the application of a small e.m.f. Suppose we now stop stirring.

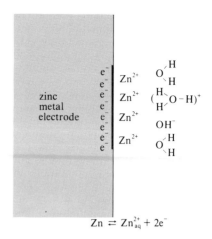

$$Zn \rightleftharpoons Zn^{2+}_{aq} + 2e^-$$

Figure 32   Illustration of zinc electrode in equilibrium with a solution of its own ions. Note the following points: (i) The hydrogen ion in solution is normally considered to be associated with one water molecule as H_3O^+, as derived from the self-ionisation of water: $2H_2O \rightleftharpoons H_3O^+ + OH^-$. (ii) In aqueous solution metal ions may have closely associated with them a particular number of water molecules in a so-called 'hydration sheath' represented as $M^{2+}.n H_2O$

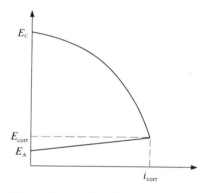

Figure 33   Graph referred to in SAQs 14 and 15

What change would you expect to see in the current and why?

The current flow will decline as the concentration of copper ions at the anode becomes stronger and that at the cathode weaker. The electrodes have become polarised by the development of an e.m.f. opposing the applied voltage. This would be apparent if the external circuit was broken and the 'open-circuit' voltage was measured. Due to the finite speed of diffusion, concentration gradients have been set up next to the electrodes which modify the electrode potentials and regulate the current flow. Stirring reduces the gradients and 'depolarises' the electrode reactions.

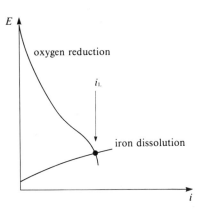

Figure 34   Evans diagram for steel corroding in aerated water, in which $i_{corr} = i_L$, the limiting current density for oxygen reduction under slow diffusion control

These effects with oxygen can have an important influence on the course of corrosion reactions, such as that of steel, where the rate of diffusion of molecular oxygen to the metal surface is the controlling parameter. We can therefore talk about a 'limiting' current density for steel in aerated water as shown in Figure 34.

Pure water saturated with air contains some 40 p.p.m. oxygen at 20 °C and this concentration falls to 10 p.p.m. (approximately 0.3 mol m^{-3}), at 5 °C in sea water. This low solubility is reflected in a small limiting current density i_L for oxygen reduction, which can be calculated from the expression

$$i_L = \frac{nFDC}{\delta} \tag{24}$$

in which D is the diffusion coefficient (typically 10^{-9} m^{2}s^{-1}) of the reacting species, C is the concentration (0.3 mol m^{-3}), δ is the thickness of the stagnant layer of electrolyte adjacent to the electrode (the diffusion layer, typically 100 μm), n is the charge number concerned (2) and F is the Faraday constant (96 500 coulombs mol^{-1}). Using these values:

$$i_L = 2 \times 96\,500 \times 10^{-9} \times 0.3/10^{-4}$$

$$= 0.6 \text{ A m}^{-2},$$

a corrosion current density corresponding to a loss of about 0.5 mm of metal thickness per year.

Why would this be increased at the 'splash' zone on partial immersion or by an increase in temperature?

Because the disturbance would increase the concentration of oxygen and decrease the diffusion layer thickness, while a temperature rise would dramatically increase D, (although C would tend to be reduced).

1.2.2   Activation polarisation

The other important polarisation phenomenon — activation polarisation — is, as its name suggests, concerned with activation energies and the kinetics of electrode reactions. By now you will be aware that although thermodynamic considerations are overriding in determining whether a chemical reaction *can possibly* proceed or not, it is kinetic considerations which will determine the *rate* at which the reaction proceeds.

Put simply, any electrode reaction has a certain activation energy, the magnitude of which depends on a number of factors such as the species participating in the electrode reaction and the nature of the electrode itself. The reaction rate depends sensitively on this activation energy. Let us take an example.

Consider the general case of a metal in equilibrium with its own ions in solution, as represented in Figure 32. There is an energy barrier associated with the transfer of a metal ion either to or from the metal. The height of this barrier influences the rate of transfer and, in general, the heights of the forward and reverse reactions will differ (Figure 35a). At any time the 'to' and 'fro' reactions will be going on and when these reactions proceed at the same rate we have a dynamic equilibrium established, with no *net* transfer of mass or charge:

$$nH_2O + M \rightleftharpoons M^{2+}.\,nH_2O + 2e^-$$

In other words, the rates of flow of electric charge (i.e. current) balance:

$$\vec{I} = \overleftarrow{I} = I_0,$$

where I_0 is called the *exchange current*. The electrode is said to be resting at its reversible potential, E_r. In treating this as a problem in chemical kinetics, the physical chemists have made use of the standard Arrhenius equation to calculate the rate $\dot{m}$ at which the ions can jump these energy hurdles. This equation has the form

$$\dot{m} = A \exp(-Q/RT) \tag{25}$$

(where Q is the activation energy, R is the gas constant, T the absolute temperature and A is a constant.)

When the potential of the electrode is changed from E_r to $(E_r + \Delta E)$, the energy diagram becomes tilted, as shown in Figure 35c.

This is obtained by adding an energy gradient (Figure 35b) to the original energy barrier (Figure 35a). The energy gradient slopes by $nF\Delta E$ (the change in free energy *per mole*) over the distance travelled by the ion in undergoing the reaction (here taken to be 1). The new activation energy in the 'forward' direction is

$$\vec{Q} = \vec{Q}_0 - \alpha nF\Delta E$$

where $\vec{Q}_0$ is the original activation energy in this direction and α defines the position of the energy hump. Accordingly, the current flowing from this reaction (which is proportional to the reaction rate) is

$$\vec{I} = \vec{K} \exp - (\vec{Q}_0 - \alpha nF\Delta E)/RT \tag{26}$$

(where $\vec{K}$ is a suitable constant). By a similar argument, the current from the 'reverse' reaction is:

$$\overleftarrow{I} = \overleftarrow{K} \exp - (\overleftarrow{Q}_0 + (1 - \alpha)nF\Delta E)/RT \tag{27}$$

The net current corresponds to the difference between these two exponential equations. If ΔE is large enough, the reverse current (Equation 27) becomes negligibly small due to the large, *negative* power of e, and as a result the anodic current I_a approximates to the forward current (Equation 26), which may be rewritten as

$$I_a = [\vec{K} \exp(-\vec{Q}_0/RT)] \exp(\alpha nF\Delta E/RT)$$

but $\quad I_0 = \vec{K} \exp - \vec{Q}_0/RT$ (the exchange current) $\tag{28}$

so $\quad I_a = I_0 \exp(\alpha nF\Delta E/RT)$

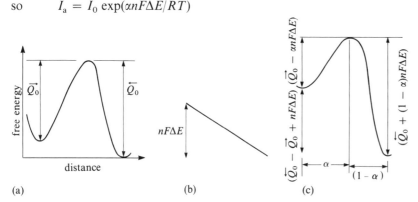

(a)   (b)   (c)

Figure 35   The change in the activation barrier from (a) to (c) caused by superimposing a potential gradient (b) on (a)

This may be rearranged to give:

$$\Delta E = \frac{2.3RT}{\alpha nF} \log \frac{I}{I_0} \qquad (29)$$

This relation is the crux of activation polarisation; it states that *when a current I flows in a cell, the electrode potential is altered by an amount ΔE which depends on the current.* A net current flow requires the 'to' and 'fro' activation energies to be altered, and this is equivalent to a change in electrode potential. The effect is analogous to the change in the potential difference between the terminals of a battery that occurs when a current flows, due to the battery having an 'internal resistance'.

In practice, it is preferred to represent the currents as current densities $(A\,m^{-2})$, dividing I by the electrode area to give i; the exchange current density becomes i_0. The shift in the electrode potential ΔE is often referred to as the *overpotential* and given the Greek symbol η (eta). This leads from Equation 29 to the relationship between the current density and the overpotential known as the **Tafel equation:**

$$\eta = \beta \log \frac{i}{i_0} \qquad (30)$$

where β, a constant characteristic of metal and environment, is

$$\left(\frac{2.3RT}{\alpha nF}\right)$$

The exchange current density i_0 differs in value according to metal and environment. In practical terms the Tafel equation means that processes with a high activation energy (i.e. with a small i_0, Equation 28) require a large overpotential to induce a given current flow (as with Fe, Cr, Ni, in contrast to Ag, Cu, Zn). Alternatively, for a given current drain from an electrode, the shift of the potential from its reversible value would be much less for Cu/Cu^{2+} than for Ni/Ni^{2+}. In electroplating baths for example, this can result in a wide variation of power requirements for a given rate of electrodeposition.

The Tafel equation was first established empirically for the hydrogen evolution reaction in acid solutions. The variation of exchange current density $(i_0)_H$ with different metals is shown in Table 3 and schematically in Figure 36. In this Evans diagram, $(i_0)_H$ is defined by the intersection of the lines for the anodic and cathodic branches of the reaction:

$$2H^+ + 2e^- \rightleftharpoons H_2$$

and these lines are described by the Tafel equation.

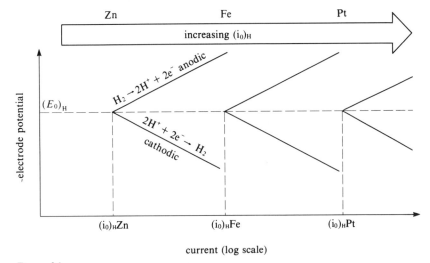

Figure 36
Variation in the exchange current density $(i_0)_H$ with the choice of electrode

Table 3   Some approximate exchange current densities for $H_2 \rightleftharpoons 2H^+ + 2e^-$ at different electrode surfaces, and the corresponding overvoltages for visible evolution of hydrogen

Metal	$(i_0)_H$ amps m^{-2}	η (volts)
Pt	10^2	negligible
Fe	10^{-2}	0.45
Cu	10^{-3}	0.44
Al	10^{-6}	0.70
Zn	10^{-7}	0.94
Hg	10^{-9}	1.10

We can use this information to explain why the corrosion rate of pure zinc in acid is much less than that of commercial zinc (containing iron as impurity). To do this we have to superimpose the corresponding polarisation data for the zinc electrode to produce Figure 37.

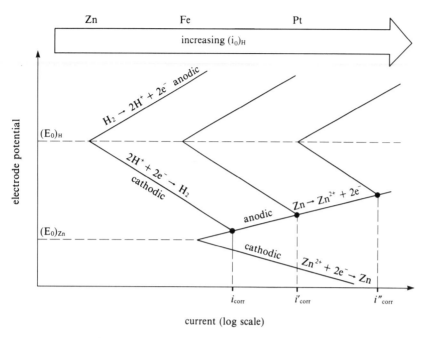

Figure 37 *A schematic potential–current diagram illustrating the influence of exchange currents on corrosion rates*

The position of $(i_0)_{Zn}$ is determined by the exchange current density at a zinc electrode in equilibrium with its own ions, about 10^{-1} amps m^{-2}.

Although the *thermodynamic* e.m.f. of the corrosion cell is the same in both cases, it is the *kinetic* factors which stimulate hydrogen evolution on iron situated as discrete impurity centres in the commercial zinc. The corrosion current is defined by the point of intersection of the anodic zinc reaction and the cathodic hydrogen reaction. It is clear from Figure 37 that the corrosion current i'_{CORR} is higher on iron-rich regions than i_{CORR}, the value on pure zinc.

> If we now coupled the zinc to a piece of platinum in the same acid, how would you expect this to affect the result and why?
>
> ---
>
> Even more hydrogen would be evolved on the platinum and the corrosion rate of the zinc would increase to the value corresponding to the corrosion current i''_{CORR}, as a consequence of the exchange current density $(i_0)_H$ being larger on platinum than on zinc or iron.

So which is the most important effect, activation or concentration polarisation? The answer is 'it depends'. Concentration polarisation dominates when one of the reacting species (e.g. oxygen, or hydrogen ions in dilute acid) becomes depleted at the reaction site quickly. When specific electrode kinetic effects are the more dominant, however, as in the case of metal dissolution or hydrogen evolution in solutions of low pH, activation polarisation has a far greater effect on the overall corrosion rate.

1.2.3 Hydrogen embrittlement

At this stage we need to think of a further complication which has a bearing on hydrogen induced environmental fracture of metals and stress corrosion problems. The hydrogen evolution reaction actually takes place in two stages:

Stage 1: $2H^+ + 2e^- \rightarrow 2H_{ads}^{\cdot}$ (adsorbed atomic hydrogen)

Stage 2: $H_{ads}^{\cdot} + H_{ads}^{\cdot} \rightarrow H_2$ (evolved gas)

Each stage has its own energy barrier and rate constant (K_1, K_2) and the slower stage is the 'rate-determining step' of the overall hydrogen evolution process. This is purely a kinetic consideration. It follows that if Stage 2 controls the rate, then atomic hydrogen can accumulate at the surface to the extent where its excess concentration may induce diffusion into the metal crystals producing dire results such as embrittlement. This can be a particular problem with high strength steels. The presence of sulphides and elements such as arsenic makes matters worse, whereas platinum and palladium are very good catalysts for the recombination reaction and encourage the evolution of less harmful molecular hydrogen.

SAQ 16

Why might cleaning steel by pickling in acid lead to hydrogen embrittlement of the metal?

1.2.4 Summary

- *Polarisation* is the change in the electrode potential that occurs as a result of current flow in a cell.
- *Concentration polarisation* is caused by changes in concentration of the reactants near the electrodes due to the chemical reaction within a cell.
- When a current flows in a cell, the electrode potential of the cathode decreases, and that of the anode increases until a common corrosion potential E_{CORR} is attained; at this point a limiting corrosion current density i_{CORR} flows.
- *Activation polarisation* arises from changes that occur in the activation energies of the forward and reverse cell reactions, when a current flows in the cell.
- The extent of activation polarisation is described by the Tafel equation:

$$\eta = \beta \log \frac{i}{i_0}$$

relating the overpotential η to the current density i.
- The exchange current density i_0 for a given reaction (e.g. hydrogen evolution) varies with the identity of the metal electrode.

The hydrogen evolution reaction occurs in two stages:
(i) $2H^+ + 2e^- \rightarrow 2H_{ads}$ (adsorbed atomic hydrogen)
(ii) $2H_{ads} \rightarrow H_2$ (evolved molecular hydrogen)

If the latter stage is sluggish, this may cause hydrogen embrittlement.

1.3 Passivity

You first came across the concept of passivity in Unit 13 of T252, where it was used to describe the corrosion-resistance of metals and alloys which, according to the electrochemical series alone, should corrode rapidly in everyday environments. Passivity is due to the formation of a very thin oxide layer on the metal surface which protects the metal from further attack under a wide range of conditions.

SAQ 17 (Revision)

Explain the phenomenon of passivity by reference to the polarisation of electrode reactions as depicted in a schematic Evans diagram.

1.3.1 Examples

Consider briefly the corrosion of aluminium. According to the electro-chemical series, it has a strong tendency to ionise in aqueous solution as follows.

$$Al \rightarrow Al^{3+} + 3e$$

having a standard electrode potential $E = -1.66$ V.

The aluminium ions then combine with water to produce the oxide and hydrogen ions:

$$2Al^{3+} + 3H_2O \rightarrow Al_2O_3 + 6H^+$$

and the counterbalancing cathodic reaction can then proceed thus

$$6H^+ + 6e \rightarrow 6H$$
$$6H \rightarrow 3H_2\uparrow$$

The reaction is effectively stifled at the second stage, that of oxide forma-tion. Once a thin layer of alumina has been formed, the aluminium ions can diffuse through only at an extremely slow rate, and, in effect further reaction ceases.

Indeed, this is the mode of action of similar metals and metal alloys which owe their corrosion resistance to these essentially kinetic rather than thermodynamic features. There are conditions, however, when such corrosion-resistant materials can lose their passivity. Remember from T252 the environmental changes that can render steel in concrete sus-ceptible to corrosion (with expensive and dangerous consequences). Consider also what might happen if the potential of the metal was to be altered, for instance by use of a potentiostat as depicted in Figure 38.

A potentiostat, as its name suggests, is a 'black-box' used to keep an im-mersed metal at a predetermined potential with respect to a reference electrode. In this example, electrode 3 has its potential fixed with respect to electrode 2 in a high resistance circuit. Current flows around the circuit made up of the electrolyte, the inert platinum electrode, and the passive metal electrode.

Now, if we gradually increase the potential applied to the passive metal, from a large negative value through zero to a large positive value we see some interesting changes in the current flowing in the 'corrosion circuit'. Consider Figure 39, showing the variations of current with applied potential.

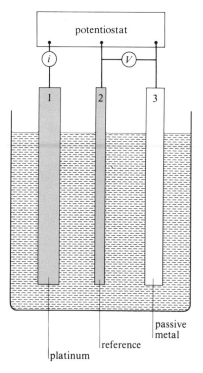

Figure 38   A potentiostat used to hold a passive metal electrode at a selected potential, relative to a standard electrode

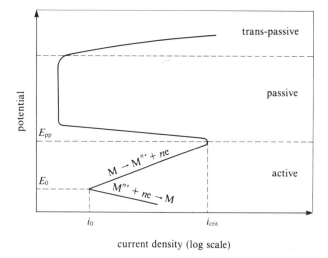

Figure 39   A typical relation between electrode potential and current density for electrode 3 in Figure 38

As the potential is gradually increased from the equilibrium potential E_0, the corrosion current increases in a linear fashion, as predicted by the Tafel equation.

Soon, however, a value of potential E_{pp} is reached where the corrosion current attains a local maximum i_{crit}, thereafter decreasing rapidly to a very low value. This remains insensitive to further increases in applied potential until, at much higher values the corrosion rate begins to pick up once again. We call the three regions on this diagram *active, passive,* and *transpassive* and, fortunately enough, under many practical conditions of service, the potential of useful metals and alloys such as aluminium and stainless steel fall well within the passive region. Within the passive region, an adherent protective oxide film forms on the metal surface, but in the transpassive region this film breaks down, allowing accelerated corrosion to occur. We shall see later that active/passive behaviour is a key factor in alloys susceptible to stress corrosion cracking.

SAQ 18

Why is Figure 39 strictly an incomplete description of the corrosion of an active/passive metal?

1.3.2 Summary

- The corrosion behaviour of aluminium can be described in terms of the chemical reaction:

$$2\,Al + 3\,H_2O \rightarrow Al_2O_3 + 3\,H_2$$

- When aluminium corrodes, a surface film of aluminium forms which protects the metal from further attack — it becomes *passive*.

- In general, as the anode potential is progressively increased, the electrode becomes *active, passive* and then *transpassive* and the rate of corrosion (the current) varies in the manner of Figure 39.

1.4 Pourbaix diagrams for copper and zinc

The aims of this section are:

(i)   to revise your knowledge of the Pourbaix diagram, and

(ii) to introduce you to the Pourbaix diagrams for copper and zinc.

In the foregoing sections we have seen how the corrosion of a metal is influenced by the electrode potential and the activity of hydrogen in the immediate environment, that is, the *p*H. The combined influence of these two variables may be viewed together on a potential–*p*H or *Pourbaix diagram*, (see Unit 14 of T252).

SAQ 19   (Revision)

Sketch a simplified Pourbaix diagram for the iron–water system, labelling the three principal regions of the diagram.

The Pourbaix diagram is an *equilibrium* diagram, that is, it is made up of regions bounded by lines representing chemical equilibria. Despite this limitation, the Pourbaix diagram gives a useful insight into the corrosion of metals in practice and so the corresponding diagrams for copper and zinc should help predict the corrosion of brass under service conditions (Figures 40 and 41).

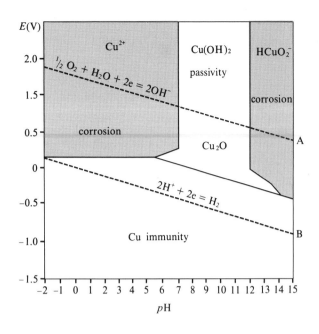

Figure 40 Potential–pH diagram for copper; the lines (A) and (B) represent equilibrium for the oxygen reduction and hydrogen evolution reactions, respectively

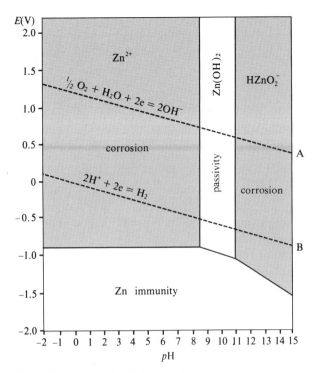

Figure 41 Potential–pH diagram for zinc

These Pourbaix diagrams may appear to be a little more complex than the one for iron with which you are already familiar but the similarities should at once be apparent:

(i) there is an immune region at low values of potential;

(ii) there is a corroding region at higher values of potential in neutral or acidic solutions;

(iii) there is a passive region under mildly alkaline conditions.

The principal difference as compared with iron is that, around $pH = 11$, passivity breaks down, something which does not happen to iron except around $pH = 14$ and under a very limited range of potentials. In the case of zinc, the passivity domain is comparatively 'narrow', running roughly from $pH = 8.5$ to $pH = 11$. In this region, zinc is protected by a passive layer of zinc hydroxide, $Zn(OH)_2$. For copper, the position is similar except that the passive region is broader, from roughly neutral solution to $pH = 12$, and, depending upon potential, the passive layer will comprise either cuprous (copper I) oxide, Cu_2O, or cupric (copper II) hydroxide, $Cu(OH)_2$.

SAQ 20

The Pourbaix diagrams depicted above apply to dissolved metal ion concentrations of 10^{-6} mole l^{-1}. What influence would a higher concentration of metal ions (say 10^{-2} mole l^{-1}) bring to bear upon the respective areas of corrosion, immunity, and passivity, assuming no change in pH or other environmental conditions?

Because changes in metal ion concentration can subtly change the boundaries of the corroding, passive, and immune domains of the Pourbaix diagram, we need to be aware of changes in solution chemistry adjacent to copper, zinc, or brass artefacts. We shall consider some possibilities in the next section.

1.4.1 Summary

- The Pourbaix diagram indicates the range of conditions (in terms of electrode potential and pH) under which a metal will be *immune, passive* and *corroding* in an aqueous environment.
- Pourbaix diagrams for the copper–water and zinc–water systems appear in Figures 40 and 41.
- Changes in concentration of dissolved metallic ions will affect the equilibrium boundaries of the Pourbaix diagram.

1.5 The effect of complex-forming agents

The aim of this section is to show that certain chemical species have a direct effect on the solution chemistry of copper. For instance, when copper dissolves in aqueous solution to give copper ions (Cu^{2+}), it is usual for these ions to be associated with four water molecules, a so-called hydration sheath. Indeed, we may write the equilibrium between copper and its hydrated cation:

$$Cu + 4H_2O \rightleftharpoons \{Cu(H_2O)_4\}^{2+} + 2e^-$$

Alternatively, in ammonia solution, we would have the following equilibrium established between copper and complex cations:

$$Cu + 2NH_3 \rightleftharpoons \{Cu^I(NH_3)_2\}^+ + e^-$$

$$\{Cu^I(NH_3)_2\}^+ + 2NH_3 \rightleftharpoons \{Cu^{II}(NH_3)_4\}^{2+} + e^-$$

The essential difference between the formation of the complex hydrated copper ion and the complex 'ammoniated' copper ions is that the formation of the latter is far more highly favoured on thermodynamic grounds. Thus the equilibrium is shifted further to the right, as indicated by the bold half-arrow.

> What consequences does this have for the electrochemistry of copper in an ammoniacal environment as compared with that in aqueous ammonia-free solution?
>
> ---
>
> With ammonia present, copper will be a more reactive metal, that is it will have a greater tendency to go into solution, in other words, to corrode.

Indeed, in such an environment, a galvanic cell made up with copper and a (normally) less noble metal, may adopt reversed polarities with the copper acting as a base metal (anode) and the other metal in the galvanic couple, e.g. iron or zinc, acting uncharacteristically as a cathode.

Copper is not unique in this respect. Many metals have a 'natural thirst' for complexing agents such as ammonia, organic amines and ionic species such as cyanide ions. Zinc, for instance, also has a strong tendency to form complexes of this nature.

Summary

- Complexing agents such as ammonia react with certain metals (in particular, copper) to form complex cations which go readily into solution, lowering the electrode potential of the metal.

1.6 The corrosion of copper alloys

The principal aim of this short section is to describe the inherent corrosion resistance of copper and copper alloys and to give examples where such resistance may break down.

Under many conditions of service, copper and its alloys are corrosion resistant, and, indeed, they may well have been selected in the first place because of this very property. These alloys are protected by a film of cuprous oxide, which adheres to the surface both under normal atmospheric conditions and in water. In very highly oxygenated conditions, or at higher temperatures, the passive layer may be oxidised to a cupric oxide or hydroxide which will also passivate. The rather attractive green 'patina' characteristic of copper roofs is a basic sulphate, $CuSO_4.3Cu(OH)_2$.

However, contamination with aggressive anions such as chloride and sulphate, or exposure to strong oxidising conditions may lead to a breakdown of passivity and consequent corrosion, perhaps in the form of pitting. And, as we have seen in the previous section, both copper and its alloys are highly susceptible to the attentions of ammonia, cyanide ions, and other complexing agents.

Copper–zinc alloys (brasses) match copper in terms of corrosion resistance and because of their superior physical properties, they are often selected instead of copper alone. Under some conditions, however, they are susceptible to certain forms of corrosion, the best example being a selective depletion of the alloy known as *dezincification*. The attacked surface is converted to a spongy mass of porous copper with very poor mechanical strength. The corrosion reaction mechanism probably involves dissolution of the alloy followed by selective redeposition of the copper. Conditions which favour this form of attack are:

(i)   poor aeration (e.g. in crevices and beneath deposits);

(ii) high temperature;

(iii) extremes of pH;

(iv) the presence of dissolved chloride ions (e.g. seawater);

(v)   the presence of dissolved carbon dioxide in soft water.

Brasses containing less than about 15% zinc are resistant to dezincification and at higher zinc contents an additional alloying agent such as 0.02 to 0.06 per cent arsenic confers immunity to attack.

Summary

- In the normal atmosphere, copper and its alloys carry a protective film of cuprous oxide (Cu_2O).
- In the presence of aggressive anions this protection is lost, thus leaving copper and copper alloys prone to corrosive processes.
- In brasses containing more than 15% zinc, there is a tendency for zinc to be dissolved preferentially by certain solutions — *dezincification*.

Now return to Section 13A.1 of the Case Study.

2 Stress corrosion cracking

2.1 The chemistry of season-cracking

As we have already seen, the problem of stress corrosion cracking in brasses arises from the combined influence of residual stress and a corrosive environment often associated with ammonia. Recent laboratory studies have shown that stress corrosion cracking of brass can be induced to occur in other environments, e.g. in the presence of sulphur dioxide, acid sulphates, and by using a number of complexing agents such as citrates, tartrates, acetates and formates. In all cases, intergranular cracking occurred under conditions where cuprous oxide, Cu_2O, was present as a passivating layer. So let's *assume*, that for some reason (to be discussed later) there is a break in this layer, and that season-cracking begins at this discontinuity on the surface of the alloy, where a small area of bare metal is exposed.

2.1.1 Dissolution

We should now look in somewhat closer detail at the chemical processes by which the exposed brass is dissolved in an ammoniacal environment. It was research in the United States at the Frankfurt Arsenal, Philadelphia that clarified the chemistry of the process. Their main concern was to ensure the reliability of 0.30 calibre ammunition used by the American forces in World War II, and their work was presented at a symposium on 'The Stress Corrosion Cracking of Metals' held in Philadelphia in 1944.

Brass tends to suffer corrosion in ammonia-containing solutions because of the complexing action, in which copper or zinc atoms are dissolved to form cuprammonium ions and zinc ammonium ions. These complex ions are called metal ammines.

$$Cu + 2NH_3 \rightarrow Cu(NH_3)_2^+ + e^- \tag{31}$$

$$Zn + 4NH_3 \rightarrow Zn(NH_3)_4^{2+} + 2e^- \tag{32}$$

Note that the complex ion formed in Equation 31 is cuprous (Cu^I); the *deep blue* Cu^{II} complex, $Cu(NH_3)_4^{2+}$, appears only if the Cu^I ion can be further oxidised in the presence of excess ammonia:

$$Cu(NH_3)_2^+ + 2\,NH_3 \rightarrow Cu(NH_3)_4^{2+} + e^- \tag{33}$$

The balancing cathodic reaction which takes up the electrons released by the dissolution reactions is the reduction of oxygen:

$$O_2 + 2H_2O + 4e^- \rightleftharpoons 4OH^- \tag{34}$$

The overall reaction is:

$$Cu + Zn + 8\,NH_3 + O_2 + 2\,H_2O \rightleftharpoons Cu(NH_3)_4^{2+}$$
$$+ Zn(NH_3)_4^{2+} + 4OH^- \tag{35}$$

The products of reaction are soluble and therefore do not stifle the re-action by clogging up the surface. Another important effect of complex ion formation is that they 'scavenge' the Cu^+ and Cu^{2+} ions from the system. Because nearly all the free copper ions are 'wrapped up' in ammonia sheaths this means that the concentration of copper ions cannot build up as dissolution proceeds which would otherwise give rise to *concentration polarisation*. You will recall from Section 1.1 that the reversible potential of a metal is affected by the concentration of ions with which it is in equilibrium, according to the Nernst equation. Hence when copper ions are removed from solution, the potential of the metal drops and it becomes more basic (i.e. more prone to dissolve).

Another factor which encourages the dissolution of copper in ammonia solutions is the fact that the $Cu(NH_3)_4^{2+}$ complex can accept an electron released from a dissolving atom to form the $Cu(NH_3)_2^+$ ion. In a de-aerated solution (for example, within a crack) this is the only available cathodic reaction, and in Home Experiment 5B you will have seen that in the sealed jar, the blue colour gradually faded as the tetrammine copper(II) complex was used up. On exposure to air, the presence of oxygen in the solution enabled $Cu(NH_3)_2^+$ to be oxidised to $Cu(NH_3)_4^{2+}$ (Equation 33) and the blue colour returned to the solution. The oxidation and reduction reactions are summarised in Figure 42.

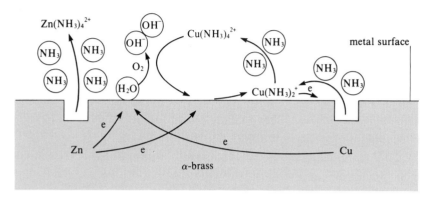

Figure 42   Corrosion of brass in ammonia

2.1.2 The effect of pH

At this stage, let's recall the assumption we made at the beginning of this section: that the dissolution reactions take place at some break in the passive layer. If this is the case, what is happening to the passive layer itself? Remember that the passive layer on brass consists of cuprous oxide, Cu_2O, which acts as an efficient cathodic surface thus effecting further dissolution at any small cracks which may occur at the metal surface.

If the cuprous oxide layer were susceptible to ammoniacal corrosion, say by the chemical reaction:

$$Cu_2O + 4NH_3 + H_2O \rightleftharpoons 2Cu(NH_3)_2^+ + 2OH^- \qquad (36)$$

we would expect to see uniform corrosion rather than localised attack (e.g. pitting). But you have seen in Experiment 5 that the tarnish layer is quite stable in the presence of ammonia and dissolved complex ions. Why is Equation 36 biased to the left?

You might expect from this equilibrium that with decreasing pH (decrease in OH^- concentration) the equilibrium would be pushed to the right and the Cu_2O would then become less stable. But there is another factor involved: the amount of ammonia is very strongly dependent on pH, as determined by the equilibrium:

$$NH_3 + H^+ \rightleftharpoons NH_4^+ \qquad (37)$$

With decreasing pH (increasing acidity and hydrogen ion concentration), the less free ammonia there will be to attack the tarnish film, and Equation 36 will be shifted to the *left*, towards stability of the oxide film.

The active/passive borderline for the cuprous oxide film occurs at pH = 7.2 (i.e. under roughly neutral conditions). At higher pH, the tarnish film is likely to dissolve but at lower pH, it will remain stable. The Pourbaix diagram for the copper–water–ammonia system (Figure 43) fully describes the situation. You have no need to commit to memory all the detail, but you should be aware of the boundaries of the three regions of passivity, immunity and corrosion.

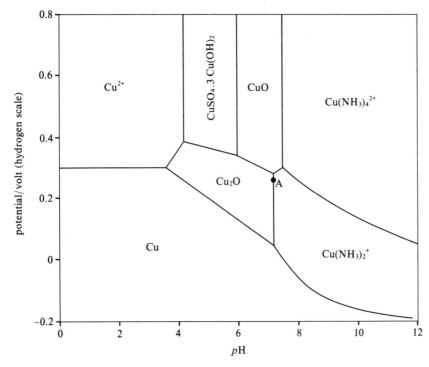

Figure 43 *Potential–pH diagram for the system $Cu–NH_3–H_2O$ (copper sulphate solution)*

SAQ 21

There are seven areas outlined on the Pourbaix diagram in Figure 43. Which areas describe (i) passivity, (ii) corrosion, (iii) immunity?

The susceptibility to stress corrosion cracking can be gauged by measuring the time required for cracks to appear under given conditions of stress and environment. Measurements of the dependence of this susceptibility on pH have been carried out on brass in ammoniacal solutions containing copper sulphate and a plot obtained of the type shown in Figure 44.

Note that the time-to-crack falls sharply to a minimum between $pH = 7.1$ 7.3 (roughly neutral), corresponding to point A on the Pourbaix diagram. This is very significant: it indicates that *cracking is most pronounced when conditions are on the borderline between active and passive.* In quite acidic solutions (around $pH = 4$) stress corrosion cracking is still occurring, but far more slowly. Above $pH = 7.8$ it appears that cracking proceeds without the formation of a passive oxide film and that in both acid and alkaline media, cracking is predominantly transgranular rather than the intergranular cracking which characterises the 'neutral' range of $pH = 6.3$ to 7.7. In the cartridge case problem we are faced with here, this is the range which interests us the most.

2.1.3 Grain boundary effects

In the 1944 Symposium, attention was drawn to experiments carried out by E. H. Dix and his collaborators on specimens of large-grained α–brass. The method of measurement is illustrated in Figure 45 in which two specimens were connected, the one with its grain boundaries masked off and the other with the grain interiors masked off leaving the grain boundaries exposed. In ammonia solution, a current of 0.19 mA was measured flowing between them, while the grain boundaries were 0.07 V more anodic than the grain interiors. A stronger ammonia solution increased the effect. These results were obtained without the application of stress and served to account for, but not necessarily explain, the intergranular penetration of unstressed brass which had previously been observed. (Indeed, the preferential etching of grain boundaries is exploited

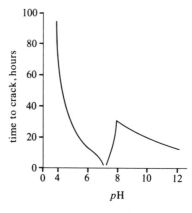

Figure 44 *Time-to-crack for brass in ammonia as a function of pH*

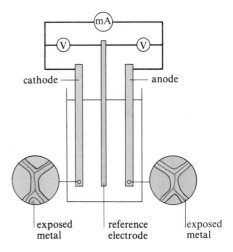

Figure 45 *Apparatus for measuring potential and current flow between grains and grain boundaries*

in metallography.) They show that there is an electrochemical difference between grains and grain boundaries *of the same material* and that electrochemical cells can arise between these regions.

The formation of surface films and their subsequent breakdown at localised regions plays an important role in many corrosion processes. A significant potential difference can be developed between filmed and unfilmed brass in ammonia solution, where the base metal is more anodic than the filmed material. Grain boundaries with a large degree of misorientation between adjoining grains are the sites most susceptible to cracking under stress. Grain boundaries provide regions of local atomic disorder, and (possibly) of some chemical segregation, within the alloy, which has the effect of enhancing electrochemical reactivity and leading to the formation of stress-concentrating features like pits, fissures and cracks. This is where the rupture of otherwise protective films would be most likely to occur.

2.1.4 Summary

- Copper and zinc dissolve in aerated aqueous ammonia solutions to form complex ions according to the equation:

$$Cu + Zn + 8NH_3 + O_2 + 2H_2O \rightleftharpoons Cu(NH_3)_4^{2+} + Zn(NH_3)_4^{2+} \\ + 4OH^-$$

- The cathodic reaction which takes up the electrons released by the dissolution (ionisation) of metal atoms involves dissolved oxygen:

$$O_2 + 2H_2O + 4e^- \rightleftharpoons 4OH^-$$

- The Pourbaix diagram for copper in aqueous ammoniacal copper sulphate (Figure 43) contains areas of immunity, passivity and corrosion.

- The transition between activity and passivity occurs at around $pH = 7$ (neutral) and this is the condition of maximum stress corrosion cracking.

- In brass, the electrode potential of a grain boundary is lower than that of the grain interior; this leads to the creation of electrochemical cells on the surface in which the grain boundary is anodic (dissolving).

2.2 The film rupture–dissolution model of season-cracking

The most plausible model we have of accounting for the initiation and propagation of season-cracks in brass is based on the foregoing chemistry. The following sequence of events is visualised:

(i)   The alloy carries a protective oxide film or rapidly forms one in the corrosive environment. Segregation of zinc at the grain boundaries results in modification of the surface film's physical and chemical properties. This defines a 'pre-existing active path' (Figure 46a).

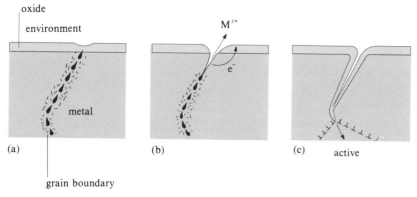

Figure 46   Stages in cracking by the film rupture–dissolution mechanism; schematic diagram of a section through the metal surface and a grain boundary; (a) initially; (b) later: film penetrated at the grain boundary; (c) later still: an intergrannular crack

(ii)   This differentiation of the surface at the grain boundary with respect to the environment leads to borderline active–passive conditions. The film becomes undermined at the grain boundary which becomes active, a situation enhanced by the stress and the small anode/large cathode geometry (Figure 46b).

(iii)   A groove develops at the grain boundary due to restricted anodic dissolution while the adjacent filmed surface acts as a cathode for the corrosion process (Figure 46c).

(iv)   Further yielding and aggressive interaction with the environment at the base of the notch ensures that the whole cycle of events continues, and the crack propagates.

In some examples of stress corrosion cracking the advancing crack tip is temporarily isolated from the aggressive environment by repassivation, but this does not seem to occur in the case of brass in ammonia. When this repassivation does occur, the crack is propagated intermittently and striations appear on the fracture surface corresponding to crack arrest contours, something which is not observed in the case of brass. However, the *sides* of the crack remain passive throughout, thereby preventing widening (or blunting) of the crack (Figure 47).

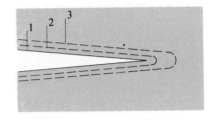

Figure 47   Progressive blunting of a crack would occur if the crack surfaces were dissolved

This model is supported by an observed correlation between the rate of crack growth (crack velocity V) and the rate of dissolution of a bare surface (as measured by the anodic current density i_a);

$$V = i_a \frac{M}{nF\rho} \tag{38}$$

where ρ = density of the metal,

n = number of electrons liberated per ion formed,

M = molar mass of metal,

F = faraday constant (96 500 C), the charge required to produce 1 gram-mole of substance following $M^{n+} + ne \rightarrow M$.

Figure 48 shows how the correlation applies to a wide range of cases including brass in ammonia. Equation 38 can be derived by a simple argument.

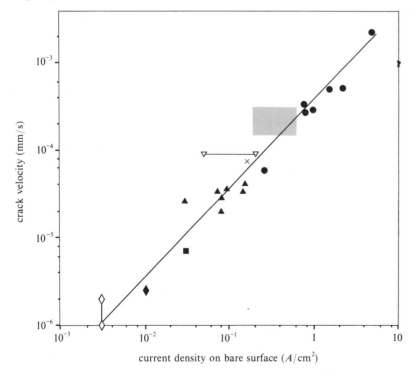

Figure 48   A correlation between observed crack velocities and current densities associated with 'bare' surfaces (Key:—circles: carbon steel in NO_3^-; filled triangles: carbon steel in hydroxyl OH^-; black square: ferritic nickel-steel in $MgCl_2$; large grey rectangle: 18–8 stainless steel in $MgCl_2$; filled diamond: carbon steel in CO_3^{2-}/HCO_3^-; hollow diamond: carbon steel in $CO/CO_2/H_2O$; cross: Al, 7% Mg in NaCl; hollow inverted triangles: brass in NH_4^+)

Consider unit length of crack tip, Figure 49. The volume rd dissolved away during the advance of the crack tip has a mass of $\left(\dfrac{rd\rho}{M}\right)$ moles; this is associated with a charge transfer

$$q = \left(\frac{rd\rho}{M}\right)nF$$

Current I is the rate of passage of charge, so differentiating with respect to time t we get:

$$\frac{dq}{dt} = I = \frac{dr}{dt}\left(\frac{d\rho}{M}\right)nF$$

and this current is transferred across a crack front of area d so the current density i is $\dfrac{I}{d}$.

So $\qquad i = \dfrac{I}{d} = \dfrac{dr}{dt}\left(\dfrac{\rho nF}{M}\right)$

or $\qquad \dfrac{dr}{dt} = \left(\dfrac{M}{\rho nF}\right)i \ \text{m s}^{-1}$

Since $\dfrac{dr}{dt}$ is simply the crack velocity, this is the same as Equation 38.

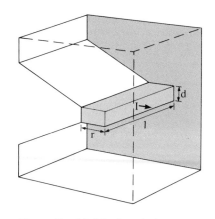

Figure 49   Model of crack tip extending by dissolution of the rectangular element

SAQ 22

Calculate the current density (in A m^{-2}) corresponding to a crack growth rate of $10^{-5}\,\text{mm s}^{-1}$, assuming $M = 58\,\text{kg mole}^{-1}$, $\rho = 7850\,\text{kg m}^{-3}$ and $n = 2$. (Use consistent units, and remember that the faraday constant is defined in terms of the gram-mole).

Transgranular cracking

This occurs in both acidic and alkaline conditions, and has no obvious pre-existing active path. It is thought that, at regions of strain concentration on the surface, slip bands fracture the passive film or ennobled surface layer, thereby exposing reactive metal below to the environment. Large slip steps have a higher probability of exposing substrate metal than small ones and slip step height increases generally with alloy content. This has been clearly demonstrated with copper–zinc alloys in respect of increasing zinc content, and with stainless steels and titanium alloys. Two other conditions must be met for the alloy to undergo transgranular cracking:

(i)   it must be passive or develop a noble surface film (a good cathode),

(ii)   it must be in an environment in which the active part of the surface is not partially repassivated within a critical time.

When the conditions are met, there is a restricted region of anodic activity at which a stress-raising slot forms (Figure 50). Indeed, electron micro-

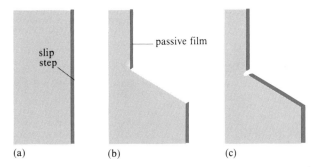

(a)   (b)   (c)

Figure 50   Nature of attack that may occur in a passivating environment on an alloy that develops very wide slip steps; (a) alloy surface; (b) same surface after plastic deformation and the production of a very wide slip step; (c) subsequent repassivation of nearly all the surface, a very small area remaining active

graphs suggest that fine scale pitting tunnels initiate across the apex of the slip step along the slip plane. These later merge laterally to initiate a transgranular stress corrosion crack.

Summary

- Cracking of alpha-brass takes place in the presence of a tarnish film of cuprous oxide.
- The established model of season-cracking in brass involves anodic dissolution of the alloy at a rupture of the passive surface film (Figure 46) — the '*film rupture–dissolution*' model.
- The model is supported by an experimentally-verified correlation between crack velocity V and the current density i_a due to the dissolution of a bare surface:

$$V = i_a \left(\frac{M}{nF\rho} \right)$$

- In ammonia solutions of around neutral pH, the rate of cracking is greatest; cracks are intergranular and the grain boundaries provide a pre-existing path.
- When season-cracking is transgranular, cracks form at large slip steps on the surface.

2.3 Mechanical aspects

2.3.1 Tests on uncracked specimens

In order to pre-empt service failures we must be able to study stress corrosion cracking under controlled laboratory conditions. The long-term nature of the phenomenon calls for some form of accelerated test of which many have been devised.

The simplest method of applying a tensile stress to a specimen is to subject the testpiece to a constant deflection; this is done in the U-bend, C-ring constant strain tests illustrated in Figure 51. In tests *a–f*, the compliance of the system will increase significantly when cracks form in the testpiece, and (since the deflection is kept constant) the load (and hence stress) will diminish as cracks grow. In case *g*, the effect is insignificant because the compliance is dominated by the 'soft' spring and so the load is almost constant during crack growth. By carrying out a large number of such tests it is possible to plot lifetime against stress level for a given environment; 'lifetime' can be defined as the time taken either for complete fracture or for the growth of a crack of an arbitrary length. Figure 52 shows data for a high strength aluminium alloy exposed to intermittent immersion in salt water — the sort of conditions the alloy might experience in a ship or an oil rig, for example. For all systems, there appears to be a stress below which failure does not occur, generally referred to as the *stress corrosion threshold stress*, σ_{scc}. The ratio of σ_{scc} to σ_Y is used to indicate the susceptibility of an alloy to stress corrosion. This can vary from total immunity ($\sigma_{scc}/\sigma_Y = 1$) to as little as $\sigma_{scc}/\sigma_Y = 0.1$.

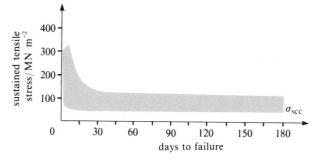

Figure 52   Stress corrosion lifetimes of an aluminium alloy in salt water

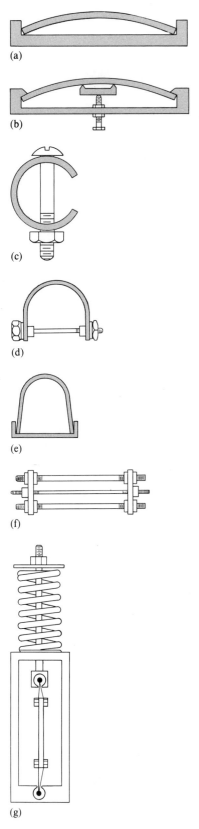

Figure 51   Stress-corrosion testpieces; (a)–(f): constant strain; (g): constant load

47

There appears to be little relationship between σ_{scc} and other physical properties of the alloy, although in some systems it has been equated with the stress to cause rupture of the surface film. All one can say with reasonable confidence is that in any given alloy system, σ_{scc} decreases with an increase in the yield or tensile strength.

Constant load tests (such as that in Figure 51g) offer the advantage of allowing accurate control of the stress but the times-to-failure become indeterminate at low loads. Disenchanted with the long times-to-failure and the wide scatter observed in this type of test, many research workers have opted for the constant strain-rate test which has the advantage of enabling tests to be completed in a predictable period of time. The type of result we might expect by systematically testing over a range of strain-rates is as shown in Figure 53.

At rapid strain-rates there is insufficient time during the course of the test for the environment to inflict any damage to the metal, and the metal exhibits ductile failure at the air-tested value of tensile strength. At very low strain-rates, the rate of surface deformation is low enough to allow continual repair of the protective surface film to occur, thereby preventing the environment gaining access to the underlying metal surface. Again, the metal exhibits normal strength and ductility. However, at intermediate strain rates, film rupture and localised metal dissolution are able to proceed to a significant extent within the timescale of the test. A consequent deterioration of mechanical properties is observed due to the intervention of stress corrosion crack initiation and growth.

2.3.2 Crack propagation

However, none of these methods measures rates of crack growth, nor indeed does any distinguish between the time taken to initiate a crack and the time taken for it to propagate across the specimen. Another imponderable is the extent to which multiple crack initiation takes place.

How could these shortcomings be overcome?

By the use of pre-cracked specimens. With the initiation stage already accomplished, the propagation of a single crack can then be studied.

There are many different geometrical configurations for pre-cracked specimens, but all accomplish the same aim of ensuring that a single crack forms and that it propagates under a known stress intensity.

Figure 54 shows the simplest kind of test piece in which the initial pre-crack is introduced and load is applied by tightening up the two bolts on either side of the notch. By self-stressing in this manner we can dispense with elaborate testing equipment, simply placing the specimen in a beaker with the crack submerged beneath the test environment, and measuring crack advance with a travelling microscope. With a fixed displacement test of this kind, as the crack runs along the length of the specimen, the value of K drops as shown in Figure 55.

The crack velocity V is found to be variable and to depend on the stress intensity K.

You should recall from Units 10–11B the graph shown in Figure 56. It shows a logarithmic plot of crack velocity V against stress intensity K; in Units 10–11 it was used to describe sub-critical crack growth in inorganic oxide glasses in a corrosive environment (water), and it can be used in the same way to describe the stress corrosion cracking of metals in a corrosive environment. Below a critical value of K (the *threshold stress intensity*, K_{ISCC}) crack growth effectively stops; the velocity is less than 10^{-10} m s^{-1}, the so-called 'patience limit'. Over a relatively narrow range of K above K_{ISSC} the crack growth rate increases rapidly with K (Stage I). As K increases further there is a transition from Stage I to

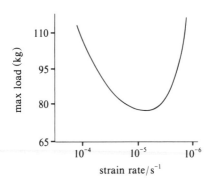

Figure 53 The variation in load-bearing ability with strain-rate under stress-corrosion conditions (Mg–Al alloy immersed in a chromate–chloride solution)

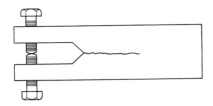

Figure 54 Double-cantilever testpiece loaded by tightening the bolts

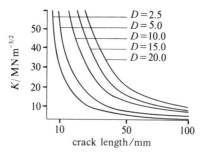

Figure 55 The fall in stress intensity that accompanies crack growth in the constant displacement (D/μm) double-cantilever testpiece

Stage II where the crack velocity is constant. Most of the lifetime of a testpiece is spent in Regions I and II. As the crack approaches the critical condition for fast fracture ($K \to K_{IC}$) a significant contribution of mechanical deformation causes the crack to accelerate again in Stage III.

2.3.3 Regions of the V/K curve

It is possible to offer some proposals as to the likely factors which control crack growth in each stage. The existence of the threshold stress intensity has been associated with the formation of a 'stretch zone' at the crack tip. The notion is that it is necessary for the plastic zone to create a bare metal surface in order for stress corrosion to occur. Below K_{ISCC}, the stress intensity at the crack tip is insufficient to cause enough yielding to expose the metal to the environment.

A difficulty with this theory is that in general the value of K_{ISCC} *decreases* as the yield strength *increases*. An alternative explanation of K_{ISCC} is the one that was presented in Unit 10–11B: that it is simply the value of K_{IC} for the brittle surface film. However, note that this is just a speculation.

Turning to Stage I of the V/K curve the relation is:

$$V = AK^n \quad \text{where } A \text{ and } n \text{ are constants.} \tag{39}$$

A number of possibilities suggest themselves to explain the rapid increase in V. If there is a purely mechanical contribution to crack extension then it would be expected that the frequency of mechanical bursts of fracture would increase with K due to the enhanced plasticity occurring in the tip zone. Another effect of elastic and plastic strain is to accelerate the rate of electrochemical dissolution. It is evident from corrosion experiments with plastically deformed specimens (e.g. forged iron nails) and from common observation of rusting on motor-car bodies that metal is more rapidly dissolved from cold-worked regions.

We can look at this from the view point of the activation energy for anodic and cathodic processes. Intuitively, one would predict that if the bonds in a metal crystal are stretched elastically, then the activation energy to effect the transition from solid atom to dissolved ion will be reduced. In terms of the potential energy diagram the energy hump is depressed by an amount q representing the stored elastic strain energy. (Remember that a cold-worked metal contains a high density of dislocations and that each dislocation has an elastic strain energy). Hence, the anodic current density (and dissolution rate) is increased to a new value $i_a = A\exp\{-(Q-q)/RT\}$. The crack velocity is proportional to i_a (Equation 38).

In the case of the stressed crack tip, the change in activation energy q should depend in some way on the stress intensity factor K, say $q = f(K)$, where f is a suitable function.

$$V \propto i_a \propto \exp\{-(Q-q)/RT\}$$

Although this theory is speculative, it rests on the plausible notion that in Region I the process of chemical dissolution is stimulated by stress, giving a dependence of V on K.

In Region II, the crack velocity is essentially constant and independent of the stress intensity K.

The reactions at the end of the crack tip follow the basic rules of all chemical reactions: that is they proceed towards a state of dynamic equilibrium at which the rate of the forward reaction is equal to the rate of the backward reaction. If we were to isolate the crack tip and consider it to be just a piece of metal in a finite amount of the liquid environment, it would at some point reach equilibrium and no further corrosion would take place.

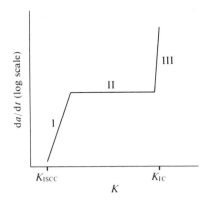

Figure 56 *The general form of the relation between crack velocity V and stress intensity K under stress corrosion conditions*

What would be the effect of running off the liquid and replacing it with fresh reagent?

The corrosion reaction would start again and proceed until equilibrium is attained once more.

The more frequently the liquid is changed the greater the overall rate of corrosion.

A constant exchange of the liquid at the crack tip would lead to an increase in the stress corrosion rate, but under normal circumstances the flow of reactants in and out of the crack is limited by diffusion. The rate of crack growth in Region II is controlled by the rate of diffusion of new reactants into the crack tip region, and as fast as they arrive they are used up by the corrosion reaction. Experimental determination of the activation energy for the process in Region II confirms that liquid diffusion is the rate controlling process.

Region III simply marks the transition between crack growth by diffusion-controlled dissolution in Region II and the strain-energy controlled fracture that occurs when $K = K_{IC}$.

This model of crack growth by anodic dissolution is thought to be applicable to copper alloys such as brass, but what of other alloy systems such as those steels and aluminium alloys which are noted for their susceptibility to stress corrosion cracking? In these cases, the reaction mechanisms are thought to be somewhat different, with evolution of cathodic hydrogen playing a crucial role. This will be reviewed in the next and final section.

2.3.4 Summary

- Stress corrosion cracking is investigated using uncracked testpieces loaded by applying a given displacement, either in tension or in bending. The lifetime is measured. If the loading frame is elastically stiff, the load on the testpiece falls off as cracks grow.

- Tests are also carried out on pre-cracked testpieces in which the rate of growth of a single crack can be studied.

- It is found that in general the crack velocity V is a function of the stress intensity K. When $\log V$ is plotted against $\log K$ there are three regions of curve (Figure 56).

- There is a threshold value of stress intensity, K_{ISCC}, below which crack growth effectively ceases.

- In Region I of the V/K curve, the relation is

$$V = AK^n$$

and crack growth is thought to proceed by mechanically-stimulated chemical dissolution.

- In Region II, the crack velocity is independent of K, and it is controlled by the rate of diffusion of reactants within the crack.

2.4 Other mechanisms of stress corrosion cracking

This case study has been concerned with one particular example of stress corrosion cracking, namely the season-cracking of brass which is thought to proceed by film rupture and anodic dissolution. Stress corrosion afflicts many other alloys too, indeed, the number of alloy–environment systems known to be susceptible increases with the passage of time.

Little credance is given nowadays to the existence of a unifying mechanism of stress corrosion cracking and it is generally agreed that a spectrum of mechanisms is operative. Disagreement may arise when a particular mechanism is attributed to a given system. For example, the following mechanisms of transgranular crack propagation have been proposed for austenitic stainless steels in chloride solutions:

(a) film rupture model;

(b) stress-assisted tunnel corrosion;

(c) hydrogen embrittlement.

Models of stress corrosion cracking may be divided into three types:

(i)   those involving pre-existing active paths;

(ii) those with strain generated active paths, and

(iii) those invoking embrittlement of the metal in the crack-tip region.

2.4.1 Pre-existing active paths

Crack propagation occurs via dissolution of an anodic region which may be a precipitate/segregate within the grain boundary or a chemically-different region adjacent to the grain boundary, Figure 57. Intergranular corrosion can occur via a similar mechanism and there is an overlap between stress corrosion cracking and intergranular corrosion where the latter is enhanced by stress. However, differences do exist as there are situations where a system is susceptible to intergranular stress corrosion cracking but immune to intergranular corrosion and vice-versa.

2.4.2 Strain generated active paths

In the absence of pre-existing active paths the disruption of a protective surface film by plastic deformation may generate an active path for crack propagation. Several models are based upon this idea, Figure 50. The main requirements are that after rupture of the film, anodic dissolution must occur at the crack tip in order to extend the crack and subsequently the new crack walls must become relatively inactive to enable the crack geometry to be maintained. In general crack paths will be transgranular, but it has been proposed that strain generated intergranular active paths also occur.

2.4.3 Embrittlement of metal in the crack-tip region

The adsorption model

This, the earliest model, was proposed to explain liquid metal embrittlement (for example, that of aluminum in contact with mercury) hydrogen embrittlement and stress corrosion cracking. It is proposed that adsorbed atoms/ions interact with strained bonds near the crack tip, Figure 58, or as suggested more recently, with dislocations or other mobile imperfections associated with the crack tip region (stress sorbtion cracking).

This is proposed to cause a reduction in the surface energy γ. In cases where $\mathscr{G}_{IC}$ is dominated by γ (very brittle materials), this causes a reduction in $\mathscr{G}_{IC}$ and a further embrittlement of the material. However, if significant plasticity occurs during cracking, the effect of γ on $\mathscr{G}_{IC}$ is negligible (Section 5, Unit 6B), and this model is not applicable.

Hydrogen based models

The term hydrogen embrittlement is often used rather loosely, and requires careful definition. To avoid confusion, stress corrosion cracking may be defined as slow crack growth under stress in an aggressive environment while hydrogen embrittlement is defined as crack growth in gaseous hydrogen or in an inert environment after pre-charging with hydrogen. In some cases, cracking may occur by a hydrogen embrittlement *mechanism* but since the hydrogen is being generated in an aggressive environment while the material is under stress, the phenomenon is deemed to be stress corrosion cracking.

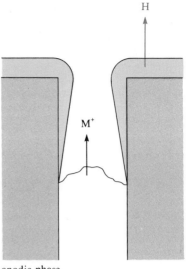

anodic phase

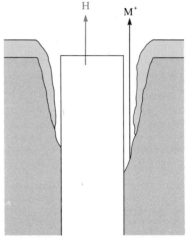

cathodic phase

Figure 57   Pre-existing active path mechanisms, in which H represents cathodic hydrogen

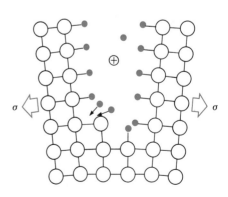

Figure 58   Crack-tip adsorption reducing strength of strained bonds

51

Hydrogen based models are numerous but can be split into three categories: the decohesion, hydride formation, and the internal pressure models.

The decohesion model

We have already seen in Section 1.2.3 that the evolution of hydrogen at a cathode is a two stage process; in the first stage, atoms are produced from ions, and in the second stage atoms combine to form molecules. In cases where the second stage is sluggish, it is proposed that atomic hydrogen diffuses into the metal as an interstitial element and accumulates at regions of high triaxial stress ahead of the crack tip, Figure 59. Locally the cohesive strength is reduced and, when the hydrogen level exceeds a critical concentration, cracking initiates and then grows back towards the existing crack front eventually leading to a new crack front being arrested by plastic deformation, Figure 60. The process then repeats itself.

Recently the model has been modified with respect to the magnitude of the stress needed to promote hydrogen accumulation and the process is now thought to occur continuously within a few atomic distances of the crack tip.

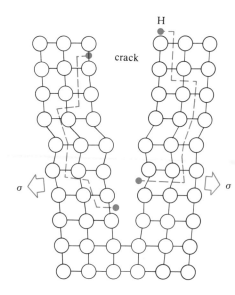

Figure 59   Local decohesion due to hydrogen diffusion and accumulation ahead of the crack tip

Hydride formation

Upon entering certain alloys (particularly those of the metals titanium, zirconium and niobium) dissolved hydrogen may precipitate under stress to form brittle particles of the metal hydride. This may lead to brittle crack growth occurring through the hydride itself or through the matrix adjacent to the hydride.

Internal pressure theory

As long ago as 1941 a model for the hydrogen embrittlement of steels was postulated based upon the idea that an internal pressure is produced by molecular hydrogen collecting within the steel. The local pressure is generated because, unlike atomic hydrogen, molecular hydrogen is not mobile in solid metal.

The lattice spacing for iron and aluminium alloys is such that hydrogen atoms produced in Stage 1, are able to diffuse through the lattice, the rate of diffusion being highly dependent on temperature. When hydrogen atoms recombine into molecular form (Stage 2), however, the size of the hydrogen molecule is too great to diffuse through the lattice. When steel samples containing atomic hydrogen are subject to stress, hydrogen atoms tend to recombine at dislocations and at non-metallic inclusions or voids within the steel lattice, forming pockets of hydrogen gas under pressure. If the stresses created in the surrounding steel cannot be relieved by movement of dislocations, fracture occurs.

High pressures undoubtedly occur under certain conditions, (e.g. after charging with hydrogen by making the metal the cathode of an electrolytic cell) and become superimposed on the externally applied stress but this alone does not provide an adequate explanation for stress corrosion cracking or hydrogen embrittlement (as defined earlier) because the basic question of why a normally-ductile alloy undergoes a brittle failure (rather than deforming plastically and failing by ductile rupture) is not addressed or answered.

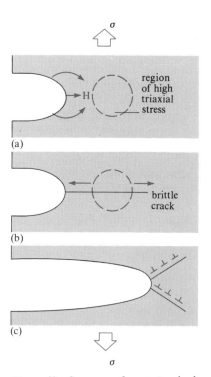

Figure 60   Sequence of events involved in crack growth by the decohesion model

Other models

Numerous other models have been proposed one of which envisages that hydrogen interacts with and pins dislocations, thereby permitting brittle fracture. This idea is attractive but as the elastic interaction between a hydrogen atom and a dislocation is thought to be weak, the general belief is that this phenomenon is unlikely to be the main cause for hydrogen induced cracking.

2.4.4 Summary

Table 4 lists some of the alloy–environment pairs susceptible to stress corrosion cracking, together with the most likely mechanism. I do not expect you to memorise the contents of this table, which, I should add, is not fully comprehensive! Rather, its purpose is to demonstrate the extent of stress corrosion cracking in common alloy systems and to show that

Table 4   Some of the alloy–environment systems known to suffer stress corrosion cracking

Alloy	Environment	Fracture path	Mechanism
Aluminium alloys			
Al–Zn–Mg, Al–Zn–Mg–Cu	Atmospheric moisture, moist gases, aqueous solutions, Cl^-, NO_3^-, CO_4^{2-}	Intergranular (transgranular can occur at high stress levels)	Anodic dissolution along pre-existing active paths was generally accepted until the last 10 years. Strong evidence for a decohesion model is accumulating.
Al–Mg, Al–Cu–Mg	Aqueous environments, Cl^-		Pre-existing active path. Some recent evidence suggests hydrogen may also be involved.
Al–Mg–Si, Al–Si–Mg	No service failures known	—	—
Copper alloys			
Pure copper	Aqueous sodium nitrite	Transgranular	Strain generated active path
α-Brasses	Ammonia/NH_4^+ solutions, amines, moist SO_2, SO_4^2, NO_2^-, NO_3^- ClO_4^-, OH^-, acetates, tartrates citrates and distilled water	Intergranular	Anodic dissolution

Dezincification
Slip step dissolution |
α/β Brasses	As for α-Brass	Intergranular and transgranular	As for α-brass plus some evidence for a hydrogen mechanism.
Phosphorus bronze	As for α-/β brass	Intergranular and transgranular	As for α-brass plus some evidence for a hydrogen mechanism
Steels			
Low strength ferritic steels	NO_3^-, OH^-, CO_3^{2-}/HCO_3^-,	Intergranular	Anodic dissolution on pre-existing active path.
	Aqueous environments including Cl^- at sufficiently negative potentials	Transgranular	Hydrogen embrittlement (decohesion?)
Low alloy steels	NO_3^-, OH^-, CO_3^{2-}/HCO_3^-, NO_2^-/SO_4^{2-}, acetates, molybdates, vanadates	Intergranular (prior austenite grain boundaries)	Anodic dissolution
High strength steels ($\sigma_Y > \sim 900$ MN m^{-2})	Atmospheric moisture, aqueous environments including H_2S, Cl^-, SO_4^{2-} and NO_3^-	Intergranular and transgranular	Almost exclusively hydrogen embrittlement (decohesion?)
Stainless steels (austenitic)	Cl^- and OH^- (usually only at temperature above $\sim 40°C$)	Transgranular for Cl^- Intergranular and transgranular for OH^-	Anodic dissolution on strain generated active path (hydrogen?)
	Polythionic acids and sodium thiosulphate	Intergranular	Anodic dissolution on pre-existing active path
(Ferritic)	Cl^- and OH^-	(As for austenitic)	(As for austenitic)
	polythionic acids	(As for austenitic)	(As for austenitic)
(Martensitic and precipitation hardened)	Sulphides, H_2S, Cl^-,	Transgranular or intergranular (prior grain boundaries)	Hydrogen embrittlement
Titanium alloys	Sea water, tap water, distilled water, and most aqueous solutions, methanol/HCl, CCl_4	Transgranular and intergranular	Hydrogen embrittlement and/or anodic dissolution

although our state of knowledge is far better than in Grimston's day, much uncertainty remains.

The salient points from Section 2.4 are:

- Stress corrosion crack growth may occur by anodic dissolution either along the pre-existing active paths (such as grain boundaries) or along strain-generated active paths (such as slip bands).

- The adsorption model of embrittlement postulates that adsorbed atoms of an active species reduce the surface energy and thereby lower the fracture strength of a brittle material.

- It has been postulated that hydrogen can cause embrittlement and crack growth by one of the following three mechanisms:

    (i)   by reducing the cohesion of material near the crack tip;
    (ii) by forming brittle metal hydrides;
    (iii) by causing molecular hydrogen to precipitate, setting up sites of internal pressure.

None of these theories is entirely satisfactory.

2.5 *(Optional) further reading*

Fundamental Aspects of Stress Corrosion Cracking, National Association of Corrosion Engineers, Houston, Texas, (NACE 1) 1969.

The Theory of Stress Corrosion Cracking in Alloys, NATO, Brussels (1972).

Stress Corrosion Cracking and Hydrogen Embrittlement of Iron-based Alloys, National Association of Corrosion Engineers, Houston, Texas, (NACE 5), 1979.

Environment-sensitive Fracture, ASTM-STP810, in press.

Self-assessment questions and answers

SAQ 1

With the aid of Figure 1, describe the chain of events that occurs when a sample of 70/30 copper–zinc is cooled slowly from the liquid state. State any assumptions made.
How might these events be changed if the alloy were cooled quickly?

Consider the equilibrium diagram in Figure 61. Cooling the alloy 'slowly' (that is, we shall take it to be in equilibrium at any instant), from A to B it consists of a uniform liquid. At temperature T_B it begins to freeze and segregate quite spontaneously: the first crystals of alpha phase, of composition C, begin to appear. As the temperature falls, the alloy consists of a mixture of solid (α) and liquid phases; at a temperature T the solid has composition E and the liquid has composition D and their relative quantities are given by the lever rule. Freezing is complete at temperature T_G, when the last liquid (of composition F) solidifies. From G to H the alloy consists entirely of uniform alpha phase.

If the alloy is cooled quickly, there is insufficient time for successively deposited alpha crystals (with compositions between C and G) to change their composition by diffusion to G; consequently, the *average* composition of solid at T_G is not G, but is deficient in zinc (say E). It follows that there must be some liquid left at T_G with a composition *to the right of* F. This liquid will freeze to produce β phase, so the solid alloy will contain a mixture of α and β phases.

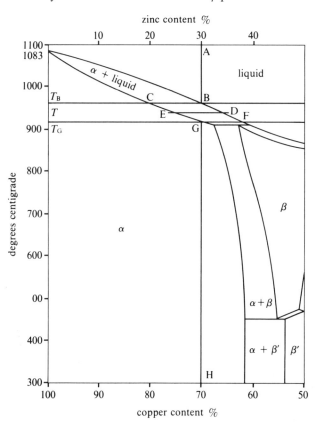

zinc content %

Figure 61   Copper–zinc phase diagram referred to in SAQ 1

SAQ 2

What is the hoop strain in the circumference of a circular blank of diameter D_0 when deep drawn by a punch of diameter D_p?

The true strain ε is defined to be

$$\varepsilon = \ln \frac{L}{L_0}$$

where L and L_0 are the initial and final lengths, respectively. In this case $L_0 = \pi D_0$, the circumference of the undrawn blank and $L = \pi D_p$, the circumference of the punch, so

$$\varepsilon = \ln \frac{D_p}{D_0}$$

$$= - \ln \frac{D_0}{D_p}$$

(the strain is negative because it represents a contraction).

SAQ 3

For simplicity, materials are sometimes regarded as being 'ideally plastic' (i.e. the stress–strain curve is elastic up to the yield stress and thereafter the strength is constant). Could such a material successfully be deep-drawn?

No, because such a material does not work-harden. You should recall from Unit 1B, Section 1.4.2 that necking occurs when the tensile stress becomes equal to the rate of work-hardening $\frac{d\sigma}{d\varepsilon}$; since this is zero, necking occurs as soon as yielding begins (i.e. at the start of drawing).

SAQ 4

Bearing in mind the need to avoid the 'orange-peel' effect, and the requirement for high ductility, recommend a suitable average grain diameter for cartridge brass that is to be deep-drawn.

A compromise is called for; for maximum ductility the grain size should be as large as possible (provided it doesn't exceed about 10% of the section thickness — Figure 4c) but to avoid the orange peel effect, the grain size should be kept below 0.04 mm. The optimum grain size for cartridge brass that is to be deep-drawn should therefore be 0.04 mm, provided the wall thickness of the blank exceeds 0.4 mm; otherwise, the grain size should be 10% of the wall thickness.

SAQ 5

An annealed brass tube of external diameter 19.3 mm and internal diameter 16.8 mm is pressurised until it yields throughout. Plot a graph of the distribution of the residual hoop stress across the wall when the tube is unloaded. If the tube was cut longitudinally at one point, what would be the displacement of the cut ends? Take $\sigma_Y = 100$ MN m^{-2},

$E = 100$ GN m^{-2} and

$$\int x \ln x \, dx = \frac{x^2}{2}\left(\ln x - \frac{1}{2}\right)$$

and

$$\int \ln x \, dx = x \ln x - x.$$

This tube has a radius ratio $k = \dfrac{b}{a} = \dfrac{19.3}{16.8} = 1.15$. Putting this value into Equation 10 (with $b = 19.3 \times 10^{-3}$ m, $\sigma_Y = 100$ MN m^{-2}) you can plot the residual stress $\sigma_{\theta R}$ against radial position r (see Figure 62).

To calculate the displacement of the ends when the tube is cut longitudinally, we need to know the residual bending moment M_R. To calculate this we note that if the residual hoop stress is $\sigma_{\theta R}(r)$ at radial position r, the hoop force in an annulus of length w and thickness dr is

$$dM_R = \sigma_{\theta R}(r) \times (r - r_0) w \, dr$$

where r_0 is the position of the 'neutral axis' ($r_0 = 0.93b$ in Figure 62). M_R is obtained by adding up the contributions of all annuli; substituting for $\sigma_{\theta R}(r)$ from Equation 10:

$$M_R = \int_a^b \sigma_Y w \left\{1 + \ln\frac{r}{b} - \frac{\ln k}{k^2 - 1}\left(1 + \frac{b^2}{r^2}\right)\right\}(r - r_0) \, dr$$

Putting $x = \dfrac{r}{b}$

$$M_R = \sigma_Y b^2 w \int_{0.87}^1 \left\{1 + \ln x - \frac{\ln k}{k^2 - 1}(1 + x^{-2})\right\}(x - 0.93) \, dx$$

$$= \sigma_Y b^2 w \left[\left(1 - \frac{\ln k}{k^2 - 1}\right)\left(\frac{x^2}{2} - 0.93\,x\right)\right.$$

$$+ \frac{x^2}{2}\left(\ln x - \frac{1}{2}\right) - 0.93(x \ln x - x)$$

$$\left.- \frac{\ln k}{k^2 - 1}\left(\ln x + \frac{0.93}{x}\right)\right]_{0.87}^1$$

$$= 3.9 \times 10^{-4}\sigma_Y b^2 w$$

Putting this equal to the expression for M_R in Equation 2:

$$3.9 \times 10^{-4}\sigma_Y b^2 w = \frac{Ewt^3\Delta}{24\pi r^2}$$

or

$$\Delta = \frac{294\sigma_Y b^2 r^2}{10^4 Et^3}$$

Putting $\sigma_Y = 100$ MN m^{-2}, $b = 9.65$ mm, $r = 9.03$ mm (mean radius), $t = 1.25$ mm, $E = 100$ GN m^{-2} we get $\Delta = 0.11$ mm.

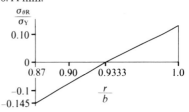

Figure 62 The variation of residual hoop stress $\sigma_{\theta R}$ across the wall of the tube in SAQ 5

SAQ 6

If a sample of the tube referred to in Figure 27 with outside diameter 0.701 inch and wall thickness 0.060 inch was cut longitudinally, what would be the mutual displacement of the cut ends? (Hint: approximate the stress distribution in Figure 27 to a linear one; take $E = 100$ GN m^{-2} and work in metric units.)

The residual stress distribution in Figure 27 is approximately a symmetrical, linear one with a maximum value of about 550 MN m^{-2}. Putting this value for σ_R into Equation 3, $r = 8.9$ mm, $t = 1.5$ mm and $y = t/2$ we get:

$$\Delta = \frac{2\pi r^2 \sigma_R}{Et/2}$$

$$= 3.6 \text{ mm}$$

SAQ 7

Residual stresses are induced by shrink-fitting two components together. Consider the steel tubes shown in Figure 28 and suppose that at ambient temperature the outer radius of the smaller one is 0.1 mm greater than the inner radius of the larger cylinder. By heating the larger tube sufficiently it can be fitted over the smaller one.

Calculate the residual stresses (hoop and radial components) in the assembled tubes when they have cooled to ambient temperature. State any assumptions made. (Hint: take the mismatch in hoop strains at the interface to be

$$\varepsilon_{\theta 2} - \varepsilon_{\theta 1} = \frac{0.1}{150}; E = 200 \text{ GN m}^{-2}; \sigma_z = 0).$$

If the tubes are assembled and the outer tube is allowed to cool, it will contract and thereby impose strains on the inner cylinder. The associated stresses set up in both cylinders can be obtained from the Lamé equations. Consider the axial stress to be zero (i.e. short tubes).

For the inner cylinder

$$\sigma_{r1} = A_1 - B_1/r^2$$

$$\sigma_{\theta 1} = A_1 + B_1/r^2$$

and for the outer cylinder

$$\sigma_{r2} = A_2 - B_2/r^2$$

$$\sigma_{\theta 2} = A_2 + B_2/r^2.$$

To find the stresses it is necessary to determine the values of the constants A_1, B_1, A_2 and B_2. These can be obtained in the following way.

At the interface between the tubes the radial stresses must be equal.

At the inner radius of the inner cylinder $\sigma_{r1} = 0$, therefore

$$0 = A_1 - B_1/(0.1)^2 \tag{i}$$

and at its outer radius

$$\sigma_{r1} = A_1 - B_1/(0.15)^2. \tag{ii}$$

At the interface with the outer cylinder,

$$\sigma_{r2} = A_2 - B_2/(0.15)^2 \tag{iii}$$

and at the outside surface $\sigma_{r2} = 0$, therefore

$$0 = A_2 - B_2/(0.2)^2. \tag{iv}$$

Equating the radial stresses at the interface (equations (ii) and (iii)) gives

$$A_1 - B_1/(0.15)^2 = A_2 - B_2/(0.15)^2. \tag{v}$$

We need one additional piece of information to find the constants. This is obtained by ensuring that compatibility is maintained at the interface in the radial direction: that is, we must have

$$- u_1 + u_2 = 0.1$$

where u_1 and u_2 are the radial displacements of the outer radius of the inner cylinder and the bore of the outer cylinder, respectively. Dividing across by the radius of the interface gives

$$- \varepsilon_{\theta_1} + \varepsilon_{\theta_2} = \frac{0.1}{150}.$$

But from elastic stress–strain relations (Table 4, Unit 2B) with $\sigma_z = 0$).

$$\varepsilon_{\theta_1} = \frac{1}{E}(\sigma_{\theta_1} - v\sigma_{r_1})$$

$$\varepsilon_{\theta_2} = \frac{1}{E}(\sigma_{\theta_2} - v\sigma_{r_2}).$$

(Notice that the thermal expansion terms are not included because the calculation refers to when the tube is cold. It was heated up only to enable the outer cylinder to be fitted onto the inner one.)

Combining the last three expressions gives

$$- \sigma_{\theta_1} + v\sigma_{r_1} + \sigma_{\theta_2} - v\sigma_{r_2} = \frac{0.1}{150}E = 133 \text{ MN m}^{-2}.$$

But $\sigma_{r_1} = \sigma_{r_2}$ at the interface so $\sigma_{\theta_2} - \sigma_{\theta_1} = 133 \text{ MN m}^{-2}$. Writing σ_{θ_2} and σ_{θ_1} in terms of Lamé's expressions gives

$$A_2 + B_2/(0.15)^2 - A_1 - B_1/(0.15)^2 = 133. \qquad \text{(vi)}$$

Equations (i), (iv), (v) and (vi) may be solved simultaneously to give A_1, B_1, A_2 and B_2:

$$A_1 = - 38.8 \text{ MN m}^{-2}$$
$$B_1 = - 0.388 \text{ MN}$$
$$A_2 = 27.7 \text{ MN m}^{-2}$$
$$B_2 = 1.108 \text{ MN}.$$

Putting these values into Lamé's equations gives the stress distribution throughout the wall of the inner cylinder:

$$\sigma_{r_1} = - 38.8 + \frac{0.388}{r^2} \text{ MN m}^{-2}$$

$$\sigma_{\theta_1} = - 38.8 - \frac{0.388}{r^2} \text{ MN m}^{-2}.$$

Similarly for the outer cylinder:

$$\sigma_{r_2} = 27.7 - \frac{1.108}{r^2} \text{ MN m}^{-2}$$

$$\sigma_{\theta_2} = 27.7 + \frac{1.108}{r^2} \text{ MN m}^{-2}.$$

The variation of these radial and hoop stresses is plotted in Figure 63.

SAQ 8 (*Revision*)

Figure 29 represents a piece of steel in an aerated, aqueous environment. Demonstrate that you are familiar with the elementary terminology of corrosion cells by completing the labels in the diagram. What is the overall chemical equation for the reaction?

Overall reaction:

$$\tfrac{1}{2}O_2 + H_2O + Fe \rightleftharpoons 2OH^- + Fe^{2+}$$

(i)   anode

(ii)   path of electron

(iii) cathode

SAQ 9 (*Revision*)

What is understood by the term *electrode potential* and how does it arise in practice?

The electrode potential is defined as the electric potential which exists between a metal and a specified solution of its own ions. It arises from the interaction between positively charged metal ions released from the metal into solution and the free electrons remaining within the metal, according to the general equilibrium relationship:

$$M \rightleftharpoons M^{n+} + ne^-$$

metal metal electrons
      ions

SAQ 10 (*Revision*)

What is the *electrochemical series*?

The electrochemical series is a ranking of various metals according to their standard electrode potentials. It expresses the tendency of metals to form positively charged ions in solution (with the strongest tendency at the *bottom* of the series).

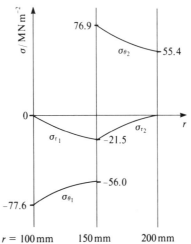

Figure 63   Variation of the radial and hoop components of residual stress along the radial direction of the shrink-fitted cylinders

SAQ 11 (Revision)

Figure 30 is taken from Unit 13, T252; assume that the sulphate solutions each contain a molar solution of metal ions. What is the 'open circuit' voltage between the two metal electrodes?

What change in free energy is associated with the working of this cell?

If the effective concentration (activity) of the metal ions corresponds to 1 mole per litre then the equilibrium single electrode potentials are given by the standard electrode potentials for zinc and copper which are -0.76 V and $+0.34$ V respectively, measured on the standard hydrogen scale. The 'open circuit' voltage is simply the algebraic sum: 1.1 V. The 'electron pressure' associated with zinc is greater than that of copper so that in an external circuit, electrons would flow spontaneously *from* the zinc *to* the copper. The zinc electrode dissolves as an anode and copper is plated out on the copper cathode:

$$Zn = Zn^{2+} + 2e^-$$
$$Cu^{2+} + 2e^- = Cu$$

That this is a *spontaneous* process can be demonstrated by placing a strip of zinc in copper sulphate solution when metallic copper deposits:

$$Cu^{2+} + Zn \rightarrow Cu + Zn^{2+}$$

This reminds us that corrosion is a spontaneous process resulting in a decrease in the thermodynamic 'free energy' of the system; chemical energy is converted into electrical energy as occurs in a battery.

SAQ 12

If the standard electrode potential for the process:

$$Cu^{2+} + 2e^- \rightarrow Cu$$

is $+0.34$ V, calculate the electrode potential that would be measured for a copper rod immersed in a non-standard solution of copper ions, given an initial cupric ion concentration of 10^{-6} moles per litre.

Using the Nernst equation,

$$E = 0.34 + 0.029 \log_{10} (10^{-6})$$
$$E = 0.34 + 0.029 \times (-6)$$
$$E = 0.34 - 0.174$$
$$E = 0.166 \text{ V}$$

Although the concentration 'effect' is muted by virtue of its logarithmic influence, the E value has been halved as compared with the standard value of 0.34 V.

SAQ 13

Having carried out the calculation in SAQ 12, is the copper rod in that example more or less noble than in the standard case?

Less noble, by a value of 0.174 V (174 millivolts).

SAQ 14 (Revision)

How should the two axes in Figure 33 be labelled, and what do the symbols E_A, E_C, E_{CORR} and i_{CORR} refer to?

The x-axis represents current, and the y-axis potential. E_A and E_C are the open circuits potentials for anode and cathode, respectively. E_{CORR} is the corrosion potential and i_{CORR} the corrosion current.

SAQ 15 (Revision)

Why, in Figure 33, is E_{CORR} so far displaced towards the open circuit anode potential?

Cathodic polarisation is dominant (i.e. the upper line in Figure 33 is steeper) because the principal factor holding down the overall rate of reaction is the diffusion of oxygen towards the cathode surface. This has the effect of pushing E_{CORR} close to E_A.

SAQ 16

Why might cleaning steel by pickling in acid lead to hydrogen embrittlement of the metal?

As well as cleaning off any scale and other surface debris, the steel itself may become attacked with the evolution of hydrogen. If there is a build-up of atomic hydrogen at the surface it may diffuse into the body of the metal leading to embrittlement or even, in the case of high strength ferrous alloys, hydrogen-cracking. Pickling operations therefore need to be carried out with care.

SAQ 17 (Revision)

Explain the phenomenon of passivity by reference to the polarisation of electrode reactions as depicted in a schematic Evans diagram.

The formation of a surface oxide film acts as an effective barrier to the passage of metallic ions and thus corrosion is under strong anodic control (i.e. the *lower* line in Figure 33 would be the steeper one). As a result, the corrosion potential of the metal will, in general, fall very close to the open circuit potential of the corresponding cathodic reaction.

SAQ 18

Why is Figure 39 strictly an incomplete description of the corrosion of an active/passive metal?

Figure 39 is an anodic polarisation plot and does not include the corresponding *cathodic* polarisation effect. However, so dominant is anodic polarisation in these cases that the cathodic polarisation curve is frequently omitted and the anodic polarisation curve shown is considered to be, for practical purposes, a complete description.

SAQ 19

Sketch a simplified Pourbaix diagram for the iron–water system labelling the three principal regions of differing corrosion behaviour.

You should have obtained a plot with the general shape shown in Figure 64, with regions labelled 'corrosion', 'passivity', and 'immunity'.

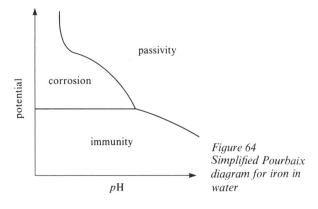

Figure 64
Simplified Pourbaix diagram for iron in water

SAQ 20

The Pourbaix diagrams depicted above apply to dissolved metal ion concentrations of 10^{-6} mole 1^{-1}. What influence would a higher concentration of metal ions (say 10^{-2} mole 1^{-1}) bring to bear upon the respective areas of corrosion, immunity, and passivity, assuming no change in pH or other environmental conditions?

By reference to the Nernst equation, the equilibrium potential for the reaction:

$$M \rightleftharpoons M^{n+} + ne$$

would be shifted in a positive direction by a factor of

$$\left\{ \frac{0.058}{n} \log_{10} \frac{C_2}{C_1} \right\}$$

where C_2 and C_1 represent final and initial concentrations of metal ions respectively. In this case, the positive shift is $\frac{0.058}{2} \times 4$ volts $= 0.116$ volts and thus the immune area would gain at the expense of the corroding region. We can anticipate too, a broadening of the passive domain at the expense of the corroding region in a similar manner to that depicted for iron in Figure 27 of Unit 14, T252.

SAQ 21

There are seven areas outlined on the Pourbaix diagram in Figure 43. Which area describes (i) passivity, (ii) corrosion, (iii) immunity?

The *passive* regions correspond to the central part of the diagram, (labelled Cu_2O, CuO, and basic $CuSO_4$). In the *corroding* regions, dissolved ionic species are produced (labelled Cu^{2+}, $Cu(NH_3)_2^+$, and $Cu(NH_3)_4^{2+}$). *Immunity* is denoted by the element itself, Cu. Point A on the Pourbaix diagram is of special interest. At this point, copper metal can coexist with cuprous oxide tarnish film whilst dissolving to form complex $Cu(NH_3)_2^+$ ions. This is what you should have observed in Home Experiment 5, and these are just the conditions under which we would envisage stress corrosion cracking to appear.

SAQ 22

Calculate the current density (in $A\,m^{-2}$) corresponding to a crack growth rate of $10^{-5}\,mm\,s^{-1}$, assuming $M = 58\,kg\,mole^{-1}$, $\rho = 7850\,kg\,m^{-3}$ and $n = 2$.

This answer simply requires the application of Equation 38, paying due attention to the consistent use of units.

$$V = i_a \left(\frac{M}{nF\rho} \right)$$

Rearranging this equation,

$$i_a = \left(\frac{VnF\rho}{M} \right)$$

Using SI units $V = 10^{-8}\,m\,s^{-1}$, $\rho = 7850\,kg\,m^{-3}$, $F = 96.5 \times 10^6\,C\,mole^{-1}$, $M = 58\,kg\,mole^{-1}$, and so we get

$$i_a = \frac{10^{-8} \times 2 \times 96.5 \times 10^6 \times 7850}{58}$$

$$= 261\,A\,m^{-2}$$

Acknowledgements

Grateful acknowledgement is made to the following sources for material used in these units:

Tables

Table 1 from Higgins, R. A. (1977) *Properties of Engineering Materials*, Hodder and Stoughton.

Figures

Figures 1 and 57 courtesy of the Copper Development Association; *Figures 4b and c* from Butts, A. (1954) *Copper*, Van Nostrand Reinhold Company Inc.; *Figures 7 and 10* from Doyle, L. E. (1969, 2nd edn.) *Manufacturing Processes and Materials for Engineers*, © 1969, p 285, 300, reprinted by permission of Prentice-Hall Inc., Englewood Cliffs, N.J.; *Figures 9a, 11c and 12* from Dieter, G. E. (1976) *Mechanical Metallurgy*, McGraw-Hill Book Company; *Figure 9b* from Johnson, W. and Mellor, P. B. (1962) *Plasticity for Mechanical Engineers*, Van Nostrand Reinhold Company Inc.; *Figure 27* from Meadowes, B. J. (1965) 'The influence of cold drawing on the magnitude and distribution of residual circumferential stresses on 70/30 brass tube' in *Journal of the Institute of Metals*, vol. 93, 1964–5; *Figures 40 and 41* from Wrangler, G. (1972) *An Introduction to Corrosion and Protection of Metals*, Institut für Metallskydd, Stockholm; *Figure 45* from Dix, E. H. (1940) in *Translations of American Institute of Metal Engineers*, vol. 137; *Figure 48* from Parkins, R. N. (1977) 'Environmental aspects of stress corrosion cracking in low strength ferritic steels' in Conference Proceedings of NACE, Houston; *Figure 52* from Sprowls, D. O. and Brown, R. M. (1972) *Resistance of Wrought High-strength Aluminium Alloys to Stress Corrosion*, Technical Paper no. 17, Aluminum Company of America; *Figures 54 and 55* from Hyatt, M. V. (1970) 'Use of precracked specimens in stress-corrosion testing of high-strength aluminium alloys' in *Corrosion*, vol. 26, no. 11, Pergamon Press.

The Course Team gratefully acknowledges the assistance of Dr. N. J. H. Holroyd in preparing Section 2.4 of Unit 13B.

Failure of Stressed Materials